Horizons

Phonics and Reading

Book 4
Lessons 121–160

Author: Pollyann O'Brien, M.A.

Editor: Alan L. Christopherson, M.S.

Alpha Omega Publications, Inc. • Rock Rapids, IA

Horizons Phonics K, Book 4

804 N. 2nd Ave. E.
Rock Rapids, IA 51246-1759

Printed in the United States of America

ISBN 978-0-7403-0140-7

LESSON 121
Review: Digraph ay, ey

1 Put a circle around the pictures that have the sound of ay as in pay.

2 Put a square around the pictures that have the sound of ey as in key.

3 Draw a line from the word to the picture it matches.

4 Spell the following words by adding the digraph ay or ey under the picture.

tr | p | donk

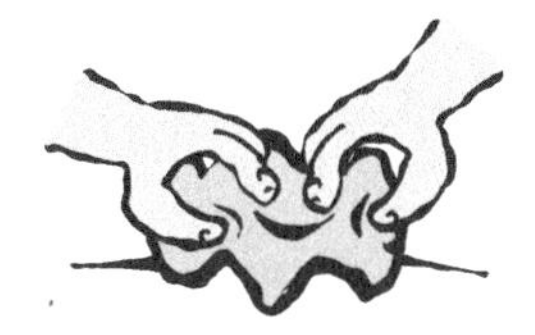

h | cl | k

5 Draw a line from the common noun to the picture it matches.

monkey

key

donkey

wheel

chain

honey

6 **Choose the correct word to complete the sentence.**

1. We go to church and ______ each Sunday. — pray / bray

2. Fay put the ______ on the desk. — tray / trip

3. A ______ lives in the barn. — donkey / cougar

4. The ______ does not fit in the lock. — key / Kay

5. We saw the bees make ______ . — honey / monkey

6. Our dog will ______ if we do not tie him to his house. — stray / clay

7 **Look at the pictures. Put 1 under the one that happens first; 2 under the next one; and 3 under the one that would happen last.**

______ ______ ______

LESSON 121
Review: Digraph ay, ey

8 Put the words in alphabetical order.

chair monkey dock frog

1. ______________ 3. ______________

2. ______________ 4. ______________

9 Draw a line from the picture to the sentence it matches. Underline all the words with ay or ey in them.

They cut the hay
for the cows to eat.

The jay in our tree
is making a nest.

There is a big
monkey at the zoo.

Mike lost the
key to his trunk.

⑩ **Circle the words your teacher reads.**

1.	stay	stem	stick
2.	monkey	money	Mike
3.	donkey	dust	day
4.	pray	pick	pack

⑪ **Draw a line from the puzzle sentence to the picture it matches.**

There is rust
in the honey.

The donkey can
pray at the church.

The monkey can
sit on money.

A dog was sitting
in a clay pot.

LESSON 122
Review: Digraphs ay, ey, ow, ou

1 Put a circle around the pictures that have the ay sound. Put a square around the pictures that have the ey sound.

2 Draw a line from the picture to the word it matches.

donkey

play

money

key

valley

pay

3 **Spell the following words by adding the correct digraphs ay, ey, or ow under the pictures.**

4 Choose and print the correct word from the word bank to complete the sentences.

donkey	elbow	money	key

1. The ____________ of my left arm is weak.

2. Bill rode the ____________ into town.

3. There is a ____________ for the lock of my trunk.

4. Brad keeps his ____________ in a big bank.

5 Print the sentence below. Be sure to use a capital letter at the beginning, and a period or question mark at the end.

it is time to go to the show

6 **Draw a line from the picture to the sentence it matches. Underline all the words that have ey or ay in them.**

The donkey has long ears.

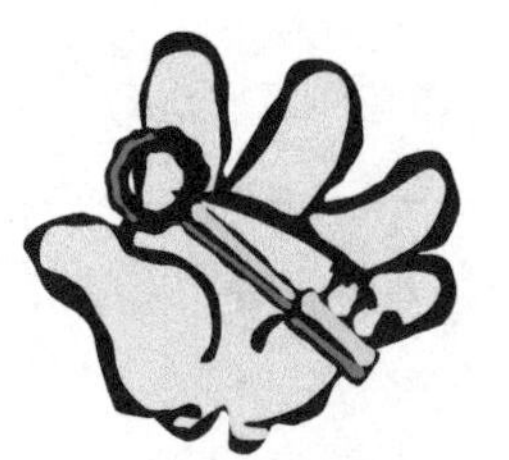

Do you have the key in your hand?

How much money did you pay for the car?

7 **Circle the words your teacher reads.**

stay	money	clay
key	may	brake

pray	pack	punk
hay	play	tray

8 **Draw a line from the puzzle phrase to the picture it matches.**

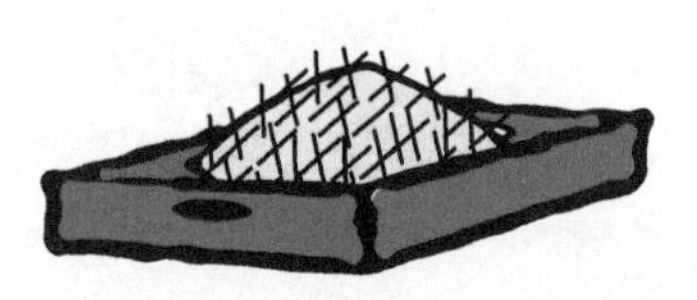

a key on a donkey

a monkey with money

a jay on a tray

a tray with hay

In pronouncing the digraphs aw and au, the vowel sounds are blended as in saw and Paul.

1 Put a circle around the pictures that have the sound we hear in the words saw and Paul.

2 Draw a line from the picture to the word it matches.

3 Look at the words under the pictures. Put a circle around the words that are spelled with aw. Underline the words that are spelled with au.

LESSON 123
Digraph aw, au

4 Spell the words below the pictures by writing aw to complete the word.

h k    y n    j

cl    cr l    dr

5 Spell the words below the pictures by writing au to complete the word.

h l 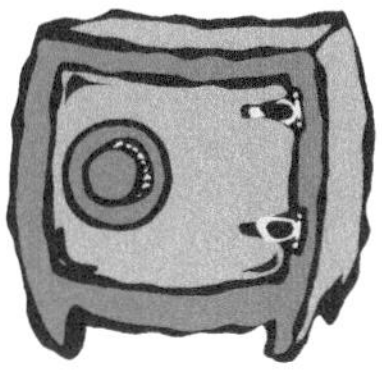   v lt

P l    s na

6 Choose the correct word from the word bank to complete the sentence. Print it on the line.

jaw	squawk	haul	fault
sauna	hawk	dawn	prawn

1. Paul fell and hurt his ____________.

2. We got out of bed at ____________.

3. We can catch a ____________ and some fish in the sea.

4. The bird let out a loud ____________.

5. We think it was a ____________ flying in the air.

6. Dad had to ____________ some dirt for his yard.

7. Jim sat in a hot ____________.

8. The auto crash was not the man's ____________.

A proper noun is the name of a person or place such as Jack Smith or New York. It must begin with a capital letter.

7 Be sure to use a capital letter on a proper noun.

Spell your first name on this line.

Spell your last name on this line.

Spell your dad's first name on this line.

Spell your mom's first name on this line.

Spell a pal's first name on this line.

8 Read the sentences. Print them correctly by putting a capital letter at the beginning of each person's name in the sentence.

It is fun to play with jane and fred.

My best friend is paul.

This boy lives in the state of maine.

We call the dog spot.

9 Have your teacher help you spell the name of your town or city.

10 Have your teacher help you spell the name of your state.

11 Draw a line from the puzzle phrase to the picture it matches.

a fawn who can sprawl

a vault with a shawl

haul a truck with a claw

a hawk that can draw

12 Draw a picture of something in this lesson. Write a sentence about your picture on the lines below.

In pronouncing the digraph ew, the two vowels are blended to make the sound you hear in the word flew.

1. Put a circle around the words that have the sound of ew as in the word blew.

LESSON 124
Digraph ew

❷ Draw a line from the picture to the word it matches.

❸ Spell the words below the pictures by writing ew to complete the word.

4 Choose the correct word from the word bank to complete the sentence.

threw	stew	screw	chew	grew	blew

1. Mom made some good ______________ for dinner.

2. Watch the dog ______________ on his bone.

3. The storm was so bad the wind ______________ the roof off the house.

4. Paul ______________ the ball over the barn.

5. Dad had to put a ______________ in the gate to fix it.

6. The grass ______________ tall in the valley.

Review common and proper nouns.

5 Read the sentences below. Draw a line under all the proper nouns.

1. Jan and Bob went to the store.
2. When we were in town, we saw Mr. Smith.
3. Jack blew the balloon so big it burst.
4. When do you want Drew to come to your house?

6 Read the sentences below. Put a circle around the common nouns.

1. The cat and dog can run in the park.
2. Where did you see the mouse go?
3. The shack is in the back yard.
4. Will the tent stand up when the wind blows so hard?

7 Circle the words your teacher reads.

1.	new	raw	time
2.	bawl	few	fault
3.	threw	vault	three
4.	cow	chew	crew

8 Print the sentences below. Use quotation marks around the words a person speaks.

1. Frank said, I like to ride horses.

2. Did you like the pie? asked Mom.

3. Yes, the pie was good, answered Bill.

4. I want to go to school, said Dirk.

9 Draw a line from the puzzle phrase to the picture.

a crew of men
in a tree

a cat with
a big jaw

a dog in
the hot stew

a new hat
for the feet

10 Color the picture.

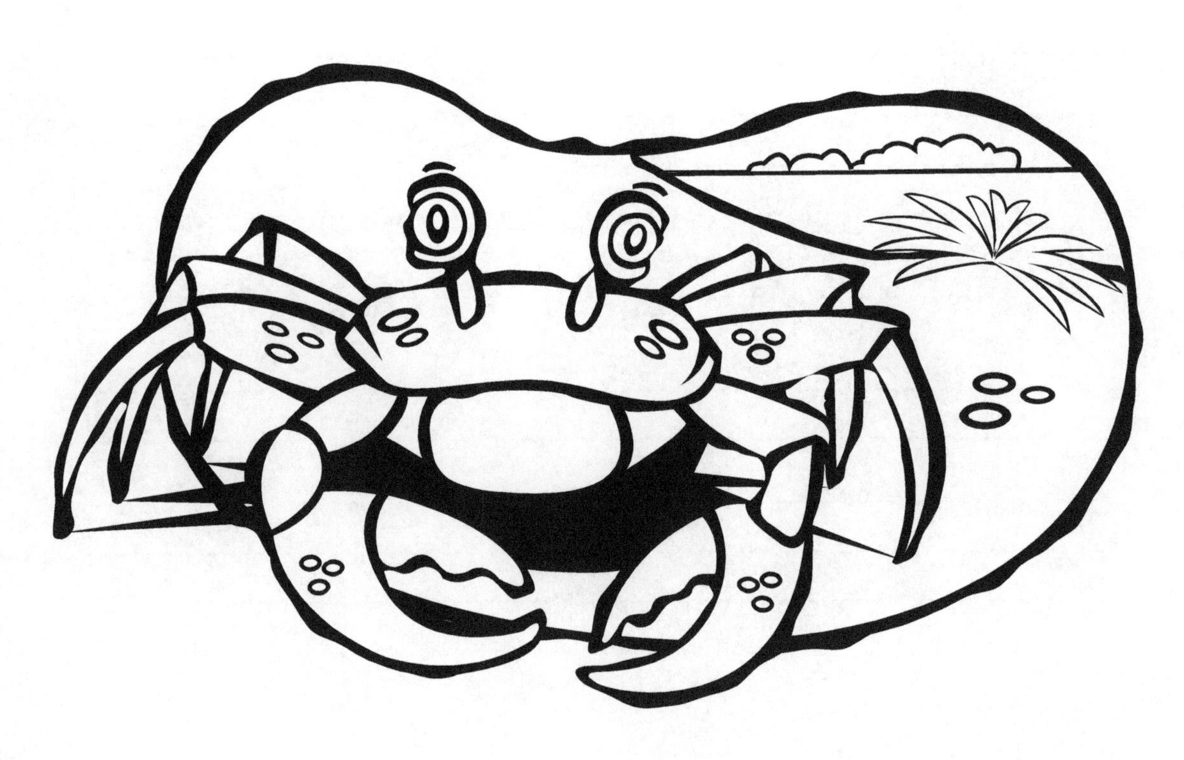

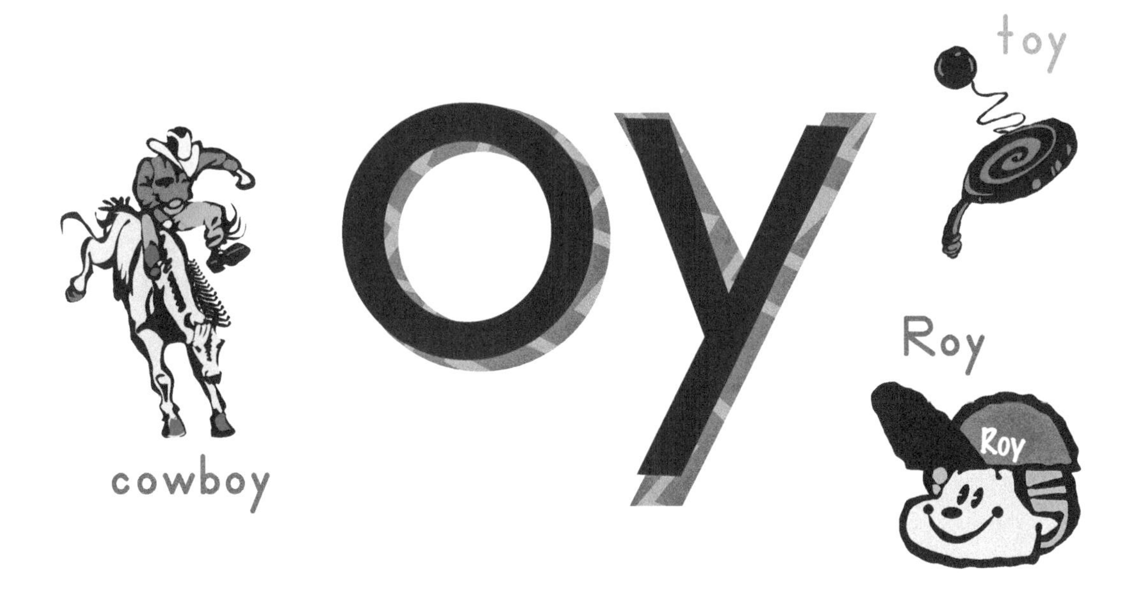

In pronouncing the diphthong oy, the two vowels are blended to make the sound we hear in the word boy.

1 Put a circle around the pictures that have the sound of oy as in boy.

2 Finish spelling the words under the pictures by filling in the oy sound.

3 Draw a line from the word to the picture it matches.

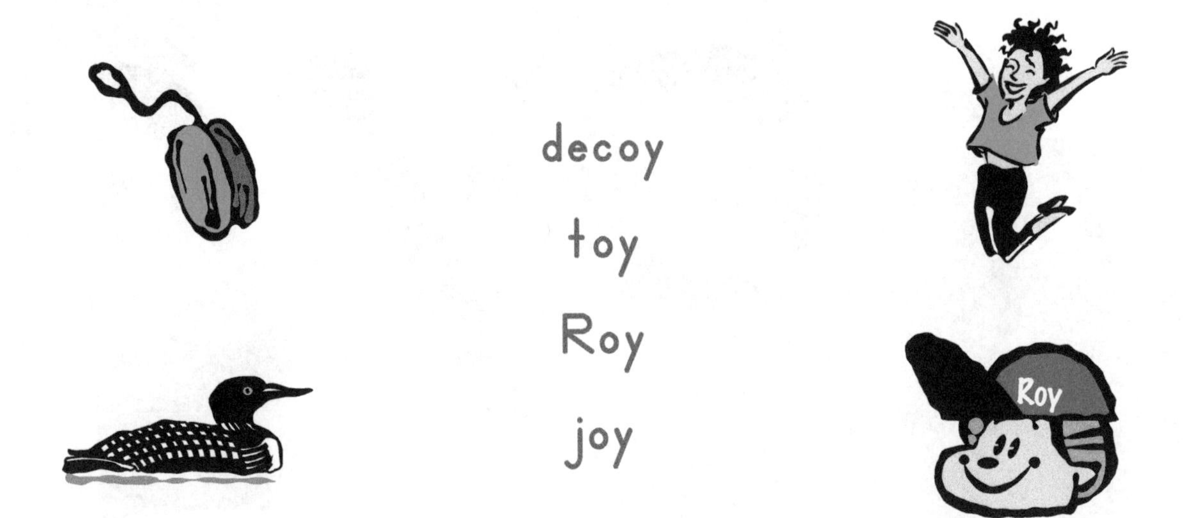

4 Choose the correct word from the word bank to complete the sentence.

joy	toy	boy	cowboy

1. The ____________ lived on a ranch.

2. Which ____________ do you like the best?

3. The pants and shirt were for the ____________ .

4. It is a ____________ to hear you sing.

5 Read the sentences below. Draw a line under the proper nouns (names of people or places). Put a circle around the common nouns (things).

1. Our dog, Spot, lives in the barn.
2. Dad took Paul and Roy to see the clowns.
3. The crew will row the boat across the lake.
4. The hawk flew to the nest.
5. Gail and Jan will go to the party.

6 Put quotation marks around the words that tell what the person is saying.

1. Ben said, What time is it?
2. I want to go to the show, said Ken.
3. Dad said, We can drive our new truck.
4. This is a good horse, said the cowboy.

7 Put the words in alphabetical order.

toy boy enjoy Roy

1. ______ 3. ______

2. ______ 4. ______

8 Read each word and then print it under the correct picture.

9 Read each word with the oy sound and then print it.

joy enjoy decoy boy

10 Circle the words your teacher reads.

1. joy jay coy
2. cowboy bay cow
3. annoy Roy ray
4. decoy destroy toy

LESSON 126
Review: aw, au, ew, oy

1. Put a circle around the pictures that have the sound of aw and au as in saw and Paul.

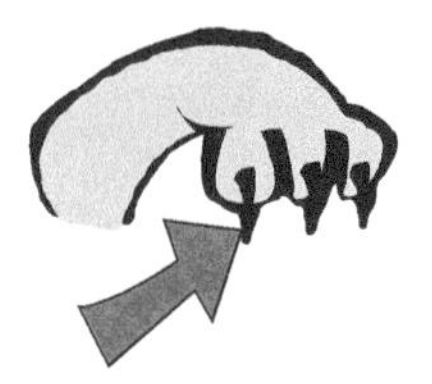

2. Draw a line from the word to the picture it matches.

crawl

paunch

auto

yawn

3 Put a circle around the pictures that have the ew sound as in few.

4 Draw a line from the word to the picture it matches.

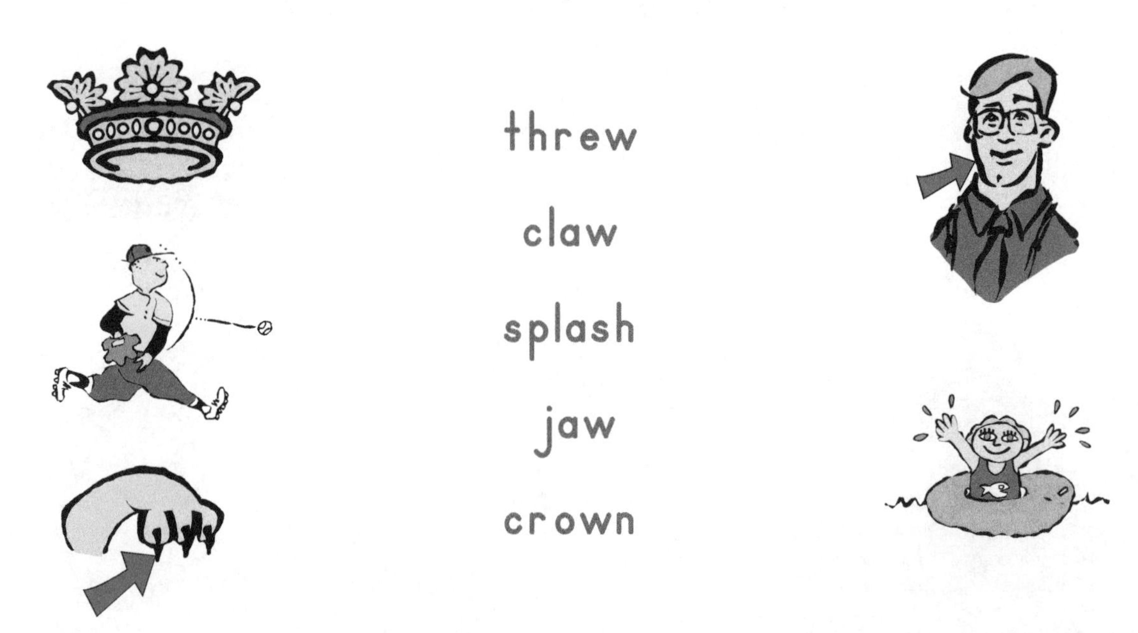

threw

claw

splash

jaw

crown

5 Put a circle around the pictures that have the oy sound as in joy.

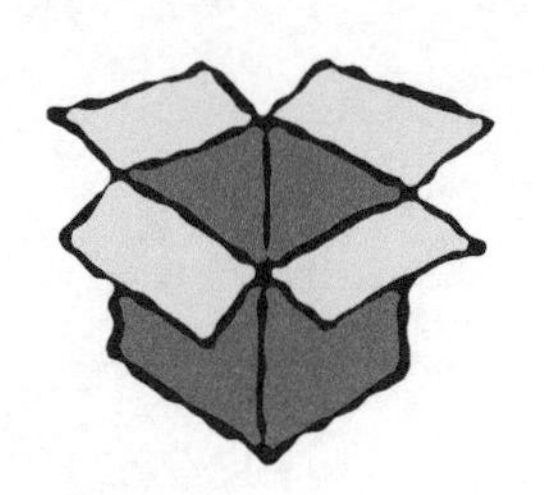

6 Draw a line from the word to the picture it matches.

Roy

donkey

money

owl

cowboy

7 Put a circle around the words your teacher reads.

jaunt	hawk	flew	chew	cowboy	haul
paw	vault	toy	new	grew	joy

8 Read each word and then write it under the correct picture.

crawl yawn shawl

9 **Read the sentences. Choose the correct word from the word bank to fill in the blanks.**

new	claw	fawn	haul	crew	joy	auto

1. Dad will ________________ a load of dirt with his truck to the back of the house.

2. I like my ________________ cowboy shirt and pants.

3. We felt ________________ when we sang the songs.

4. The ________________ on the hawk was sharp.

5. Did you see the ________________ work hard on the roads?

6. A ________________ is a baby deer.

7. The new red ________________ can go fast.

⑩ Read each word with the aw sound and then write it.

prawn law raw hawk fawn lawn

⑪ Read each word and then write it under the correct picture.

jaunt gauze paunch

⑫ Read each word with the au sound and then write it.

Paul auto haul fault vault paunch

13 Read each word and then write it under the correct picture.

destroy toy enjoy

14 Read each word with the oy sound and then write it.

cowboy joy Roy decoy

15 Print the words from the word bank that rhyme with the words.

new	gaunt	fawn	drawn	few
haunt	lawn	threw	taunt	

chew

dawn

jaunt

In pronouncing the diphthong oi, the two vowels are blended to make the sound we hear in the word oil.

1. Put a circle around the pictures that have the sound of oi as in oil. Underline the oi in each word.

2 Draw a line from the word to the picture it matches.

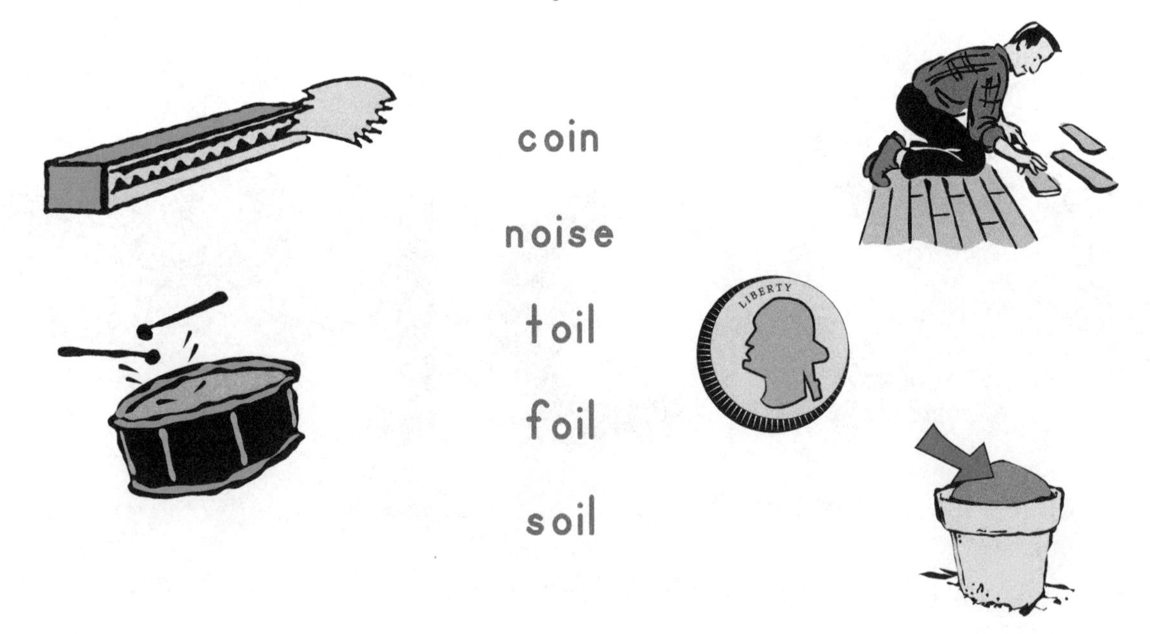

coin

noise

toil

foil

soil

3 Practice printing words with oi in them. Underline oi in each word.

spoil	point	boil	join
moist	broil	toil	joint

4 Read the sentences. Underline the words that have oi in them.

The soil is good for the plants to grow.

Jake had a coin in his hand.

A car must have oil in it to run well.

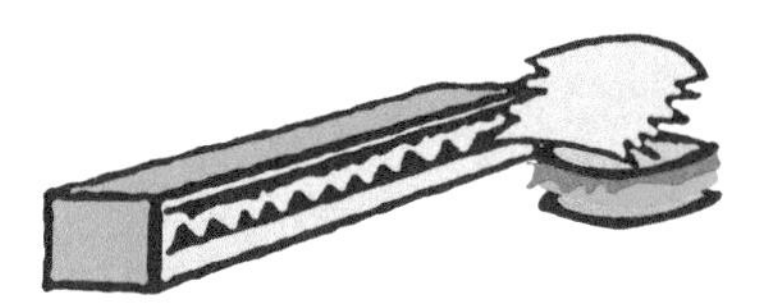

The foil was on top of the food.

5 Draw a line from the puzzle phrase to the picture it matches.

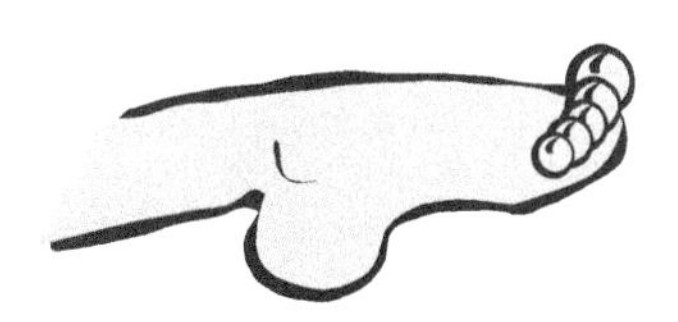

point with your foot

join a pig with an oink

toil in the oil

6 **Spell the correct word from the word bank below each picture. Then print the rest of the words on the lines below.**

boil	broil	coin	voice	toil
void	poison	joint	noise	join

7 Read the sentences with your teacher. From the word bank, print the vocabulary word that tells about the sentence.

broil	toil	coin	join	boil	moist

1. Jim is glad he has a good job where he can work.
2. Fern saved her money to put in her bank.
3. We put the meat in the oven to cook.
4. All the boys will meet in the clubhouse.
5. Mom cooked the beans in water on top of the stove.
6. The ground was damp.

8 **Print the sentences below. Be sure to use a capital letter at the beginning, and a period or question mark at the end.**

a pig makes the noise we call an "oink"

did you join the group

9 **Follow the letters and connect the dots to make a picture. Color the picture.**

Review: ow, ou, ay, ey

1 Put a circle around the pictures that have the ow sound, as in cow.

2 Put an x under the pictures that have the long ō sound, as in flow.

3 Put a square around the pictures that have the ou sound, as in house.

4 Underline the pictures that have the ay sound, as in stay.

5 Underline the pictures that have the ey sound, as in valley.

6 Put the words in alphabetical order.

growl drown haul shout

1. ______________ 3. ______________

2. ______________ 4. ______________

7 Choose the correct word to complete the sentence.
Print it on the line.

1. The dog will ________ away from home if we are mean to her. — stray / strike

2. The ________ can swing by its tail. — monkey / donkey

3. Which ________ do you like best? — destroy / toy

4. We get our milk from the ________. — clouds / cows

5. The lady ran from the little gray ________. — mouse / flower

8 Circle the words your teacher reads.

1.	couch	town	flower
2.	flour	key	blow
3.	elbow	hound	float
4.	rainbow	pound	stay

9 Print the words that rhyme from the word bank.

howl	now	snow	hour
plow	sour	prowl	grow

owl

cow

show

flour

10 Print the sentence below. Be sure to use a capital letter at the beginning, and a period or question mark at the end.

will the crowd clap for Dan when he sings

11 **Draw a line from the picture to the sentence it matches.**

Where does the owl have its nest?

A flower can be yellow, blue, pink, or red.

The crow can fly far away.

This pig has a funny snout that sticks out.

All the boys can throw the rocks in the stream.

Did the donkey go back into the barn?

LESSON 129
Review: Digraphs aw, au, ew

1 Put a circle around the pictures that have the aw sound as in saw.

2 Put a circle around the pictures that have the au sound as in fault.

3. Underline the pictures that have the ew sound as in new.

4. Draw a line from the word to the picture it matches.

LESSON 129
Review: Digraphs aw, au, ew

5 Choose the correct word to complete the sentence.

Print it on the line.

1. The lady ______ the shawl over her arms. — threw / think

2. Mom has a big ______ in her ring. — jet / jewel

3. Did you help ______ the toys into the chest? — throw / haul

4. When Paul does not get his sleep, we see him ______. — yawn / yes

5. Did the boy ______ his food? — chew / chow

6. The bank has a ______ to keep the money safe. — vault / fault

6 **Print the sentences. Put quotation marks to show the words that are spoken.**

Paul said, Did you see the hawk?

No, said Ben. I did not see any birds.

7 **Draw a line from the puzzle phrase to the picture it matches.**

chew the rope

claw the straw

haul a fawn

a screw flew

a paw in a vault

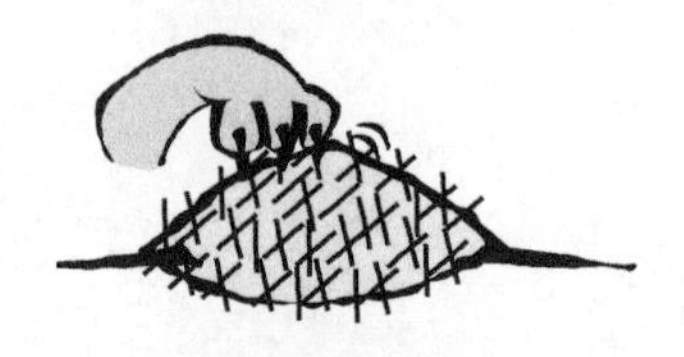

8 Spell the correct word from the word bank below each picture.

Then print the rest of the words on the lines below.

stew	paw	vault	haul
chew	draw	claw	pew

9 Circle the words your teacher reads.

1.	jewel	haunt	sauna
2.	stew	auto	crawl
3.	gauze	screw	flaw

10 Draw a picture. Write a sentence about your picture on the lines below.

Review: ow, ou

1. Put a circle around the pictures that have ow and make a long ō sound as in show.

2. Underline the pictures that have the ou sound as in out.

   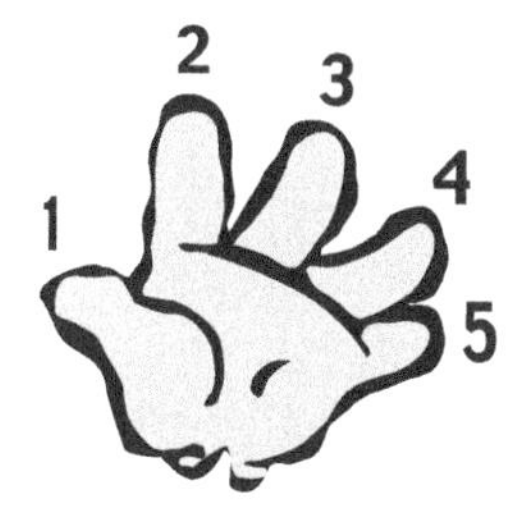

3 Draw a line from the word to the picture it matches.

Spell the word below each picture.

arrow

pillow

shadow

window

4 Draw a line from the word to the picture it matches.

Spell the word below each picture.

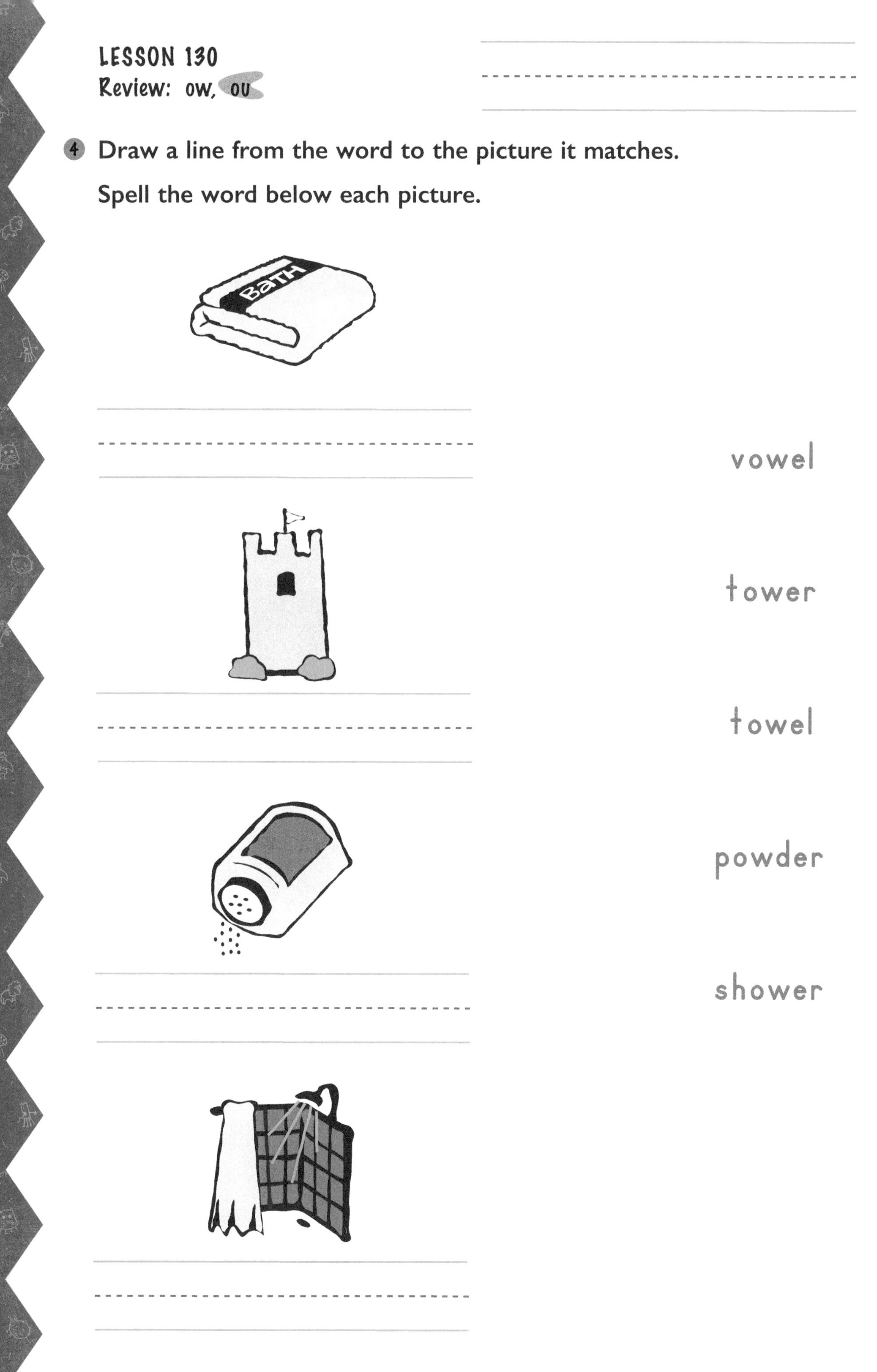

5 Put a square around the pictures that have the ow sound as in how.

6 Read the sentences. Underline the words that have ou in them.

1. We live in a new house.
2. Dad got a trout when he went to the lake to fish.
3. The peach is round.
4. The cloud in the sky is white.

7 Read the sentences. Put a circle around the words that have ow and make a long ō sound.

1. The sun is low in the sky.
2. There is a rainbow that has yellow, blue, and red in it.
3. Jan's left elbow hurts.
4. Look out the window and you can see the shadow.

LESSON 130
Review: ow, ou

8 Draw a line from the word to the picture it matches.

Spell the word below each picture.

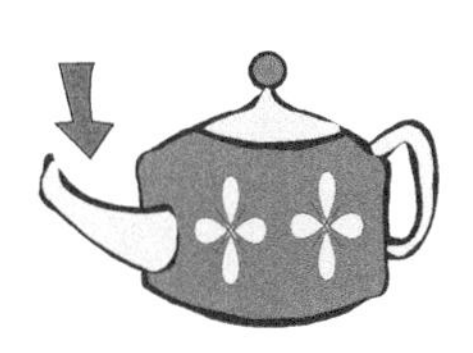

pound

hound

couch

spout

round

9 Circle the words your teacher reads.

1.	pillow	row	blow
2.	flow	arrow	window
3.	horse	house	hang
4.	yellow	shout	found

⑩ **Draw a line from the puzzle phrase to the picture it matches.**

mow the rocks

step on
a shadow

a bow on a bowl

a crow on
a rainbow

⑪ **Print the sentences. Be sure to use a capital letter at the beginning and a period or question mark at the end.**

did you look out the window

jack is proud to be a scout

1 Put a circle around the pictures that have the oy sound as in joy or the oi sound as in noise.

2 Draw a line from the word to the picture it matches.

Spell the word below each picture.

employ

toy

cowboy

Roy

annoy

3 Put a square around the pictures that have the oi sound as in toil.

4 Circle the words your teacher reads.

toy	boil	joy
spoil	oink	groin
enjoy	annoy	destroy
cowboy	employ	soy

5 On the lines below print the words from the word bank that rhyme.

destroy	soil	boy	boil	cowboy	foil

oil

toy

6 Draw a line from the word to the picture it matches.

Spell the word below each picture.

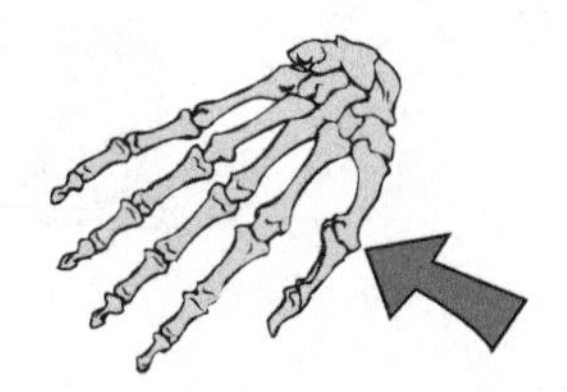

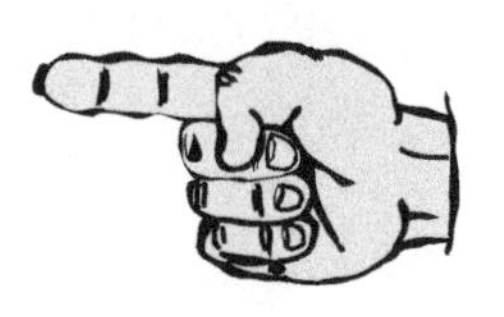

broil

point

joint

moist

voice

noise

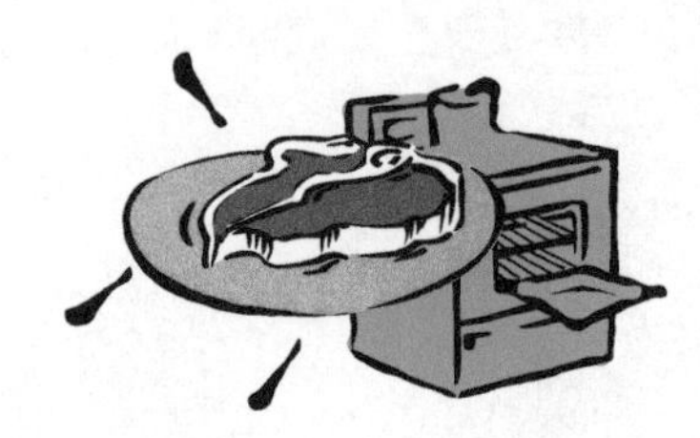

7 Read the sentences. Underline the words that have oy or oi sound in the word.

1. Peg has to boil the beets until they are cooked.
2. Dad will broil the fish for dinner.
3. The jet crash can destroy a house.
4. How many men did the man employ?
5. The cowboy likes to ride a donkey.
6. The meat will spoil if you do not put it away.
7. The man at the shop put oil in Dad's auto.

8 Look at the sentences. On the lines below, print the one sentence that matches the picture.

1. The ground is too moist to plant flowers.
2. Mom will plant beets in the garden.
3. Dad will spray the dirt to make a flower garden.
4. This plant has sharp points.

9 Print the sentences. Be sure to use a capital letter at the beginning and a question mark or period at the end.

when did you put the dinner on to boil

when I get big, I want to be a cowboy

Rule: The letter y at the end of a word can change the sound and make the sound of a long ī.

1 Put a circle around the pictures that have the letter y that makes the sound of long ī as in cry.

2 Spell the correct word below each picture. Then print the rest of the words on the lines below.

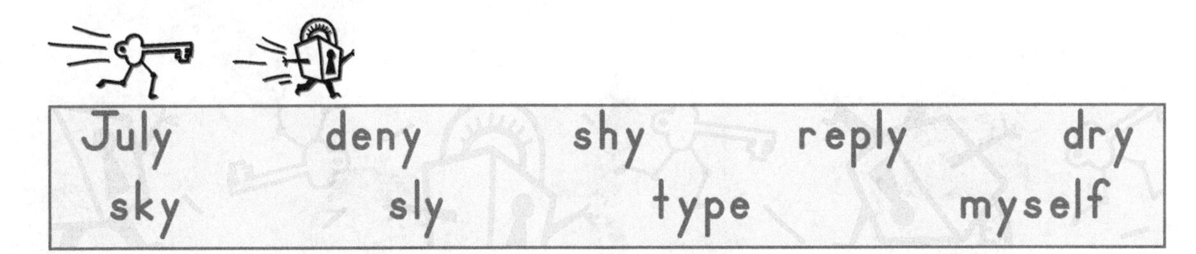

July deny shy reply dry
sky sly type myself

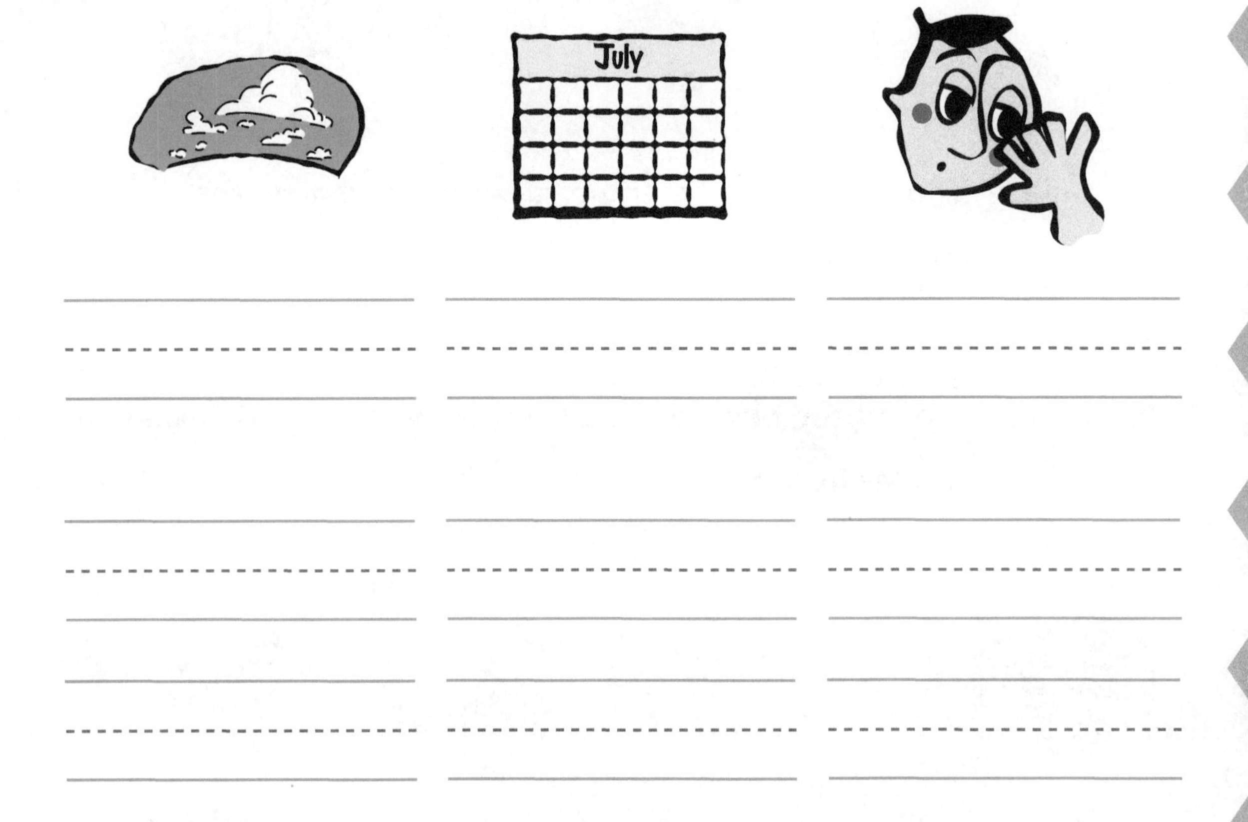

3 Circle the words your teacher reads.

pry	shy	sky
baby	by	dry

my	fly	deny
sunny	daddy	why

LESSON 132
Letter y: cry

4 Draw a line from the word to the picture it matches.

cry
dry
fly
fry
type

5 Read the sentences. Choose and print the word to make the sentence correct.

1. We were sorry to hear the baby ________. — cry / deny

2. I like to read a book all by ________. — herself / myself

3. The stars are pretty in the ________. — sky / shy

4. Don likes to see the birds ________ to the nests. — why / fly

5. I will ________ to do my best. — try / spy

6 **Read the sentences with your teacher. From the word bank, print the vocabulary word that tells about the sentence.**

fly	reply	dry	deny	cry

1. The baby is sad when she goes to bed at night. ____________
2. We did not want to stay wet after we took a bath. ____________
3. Birds do not have to walk or run to get where they want to go. ____________
4. Bill told his mom he did not drop the vase. ____________
5. When someone asks you a question, you must answer. ____________

7 **Write the same sentence by putting your name in place of Dave.**

Dave will always try to do what is best.

LESSON 133
Letter y: baby

Rule: The letter y at the end of a word can change the sound and make it say a long ē.

❶ **Put a circle around the pictures that have the ending letter y that makes the long ē sound, as in baby.**

2 Spell the correct word from the word bank below each picture. Then print the rest of the words on the lines below.

army	city	skinny	easy	empty
sorry	dizzy	fussy	pretty	safety

LESSON 133

Letter y: baby

3 Draw a line from the word to the picture it matches.

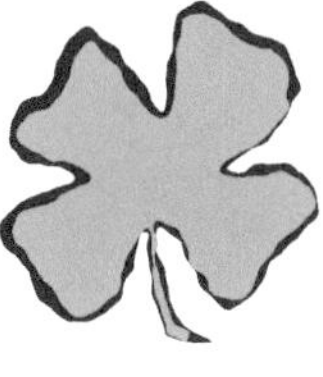

January

lucky

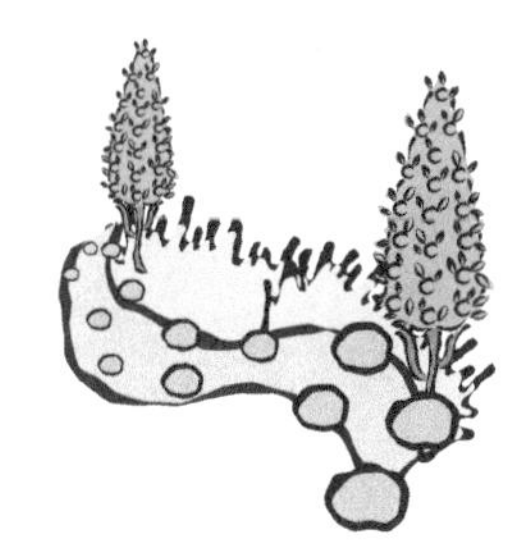

rainy

party

sunny

cloudy

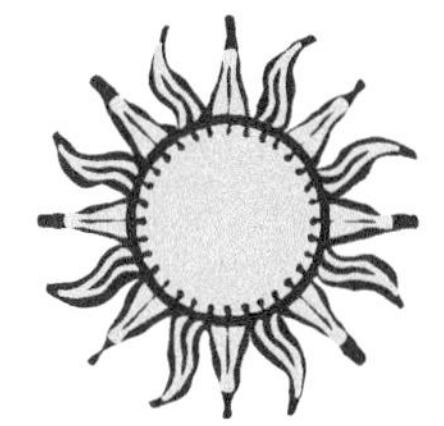

rocky

4 Print the words from the word bank that rhyme.

funny	musty	handy	carry

candy ------------------------ rusty ------------------------

sunny ------------------------ marry------------------------

5 **Read the sentences with your teacher. From the word bank, print the vocabulary word that tells about the picture.**

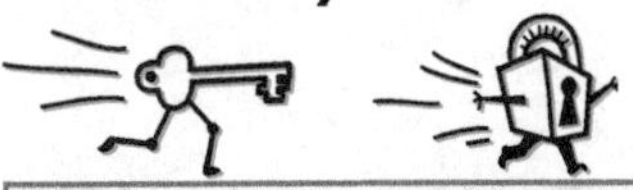

happy	puppy	dizzy	candy	empty	study

1. The baby dog was hungry. ______________

2. There was not a drop of milk for lunch. ______________

3. Bob got a sweet treat at the store. ______________

4. The merry-go-round made the kids feel funny. ______________

5. You can learn a lot when you read books. ______________

6. Every day something good happens to me. ______________

LESSON 133
Letter y: baby

6 Read the sentences. Choose and print the word to make the sentence correct.

1. The bride and groom will ________ this morning. marry musty

2. We could hear the ________ bark and growl. rainy puppy

3. It makes me ________ when I sing. hungry happy

4. The ________ was very good to eat. candy carry

5. We got wet when we went out on a ________ day. rainy rocky

6. Don gets ________ when he stays up too late. shady sleepy

7 Circle the words your teacher reads.

1.	army	baby	happy
2.	fussy	lucky	party
3.	sunny	windy	cloudy
4.	speedy	tricky	easy

8 Write the same sentence by putting your name in place of Becky.

Becky said, "I am a lucky person."

LESSON 134
Review: Letter y; cry, baby

1 Put a circle around the pictures that have a y with the long ī sound.
Put a square around the pictures that have a y with the long ē sound.

2 Circle the words your teacher reads.

fussy lucky study	puppy dusty rainy
cry try why	funny marry many

3. Print the words from the word bank in columns.

puppy	sky	baby	deny
study	July	army	fry

y with long ē sound	y with long ī sound

4. Spell the words from the word bank under the pictures.

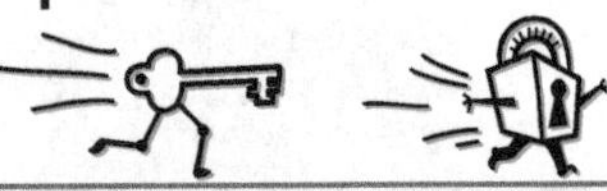

fly	cry	spy

LESSON 134
Review: Letter y; cry, baby

5 **Choose and print the correct word on the line in each sentence.**

1. The ________ will sleep in the crib. — baby / type

2. I want to see the birds ________ to the trees. — easy / fly

3. My birthday is in ________. — defy / July

4. The milk is all gone so the glass is ________. — empty / enemy

5. The girl was so ________ she had to eat more. — skinny / why

6. All the boys and girls will ________ to read the books. — try / very

7. The red and yellow roses are very ________. — party / pretty

6 Print the following sentences using capital letters for the proper nouns.

The boy said, "My name is danny."

jane has a new puppy.

Lots of boys and girls live in the state of maine.

7 Have your teacher help you write a sentence using your own name.

LESSON 135
Vowel Digraph Special oo: book

Rule: The vowel digraph oo has two different sounds.
1. The oo sound is short as in book.
2. The oo sound is long as in tooth.

1 Read each word under the picture and then write it on the lines below.

2 Read the sentences with your teacher. Underline the words that have the short oo sound as in book.

1. I took so long to get ready that I was late.
2. The nook in the park had benches made of wood.
3. Did you take a look in that big red book?
4. There is a crook in the branch of the tree.
5. Mom can cook the meat just the way we like it.
6. We were so cold we shook all over.
7. Dave had a hood on his coat.
8. My foot has five toes.
9. The farmers shear the wool from the sheep every year.
10. There were many fish swimming in the brook.
11. The baby stood too close to the pond.

3 Circle the words your teacher reads.

good	soot	crook	book	took	shook
cook	wool	look	stood	hook	wood

4 Read each word and then write it under the correct picture.

foot book stood cook

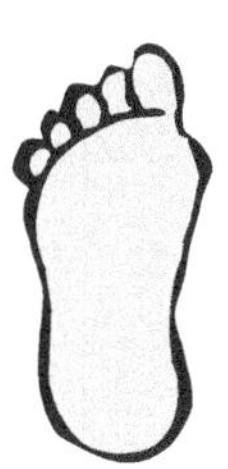

5 Print the words from the word bank that rhyme.

book	wood	stood	took	look	hood

good

cook

6 Read the sentences with your teacher. From the word bank, print the vocabulary word that tells about the sentence.

cook	hook	brook	nook	book	stood

1. It is a good idea to study the things you read in school. ______

2. We went to a special place in the park to watch the birds. ______

3. Hang your coat up every time you take it off. ______

4. You have to get your meals ready to eat. ______

5. Dan can fish in places other than just a lake or pond. ______

6. He did not want to sit down, he wanted to stand up. ______

Review Rule: The vowel digraph oo has two different sounds.

1. The oo sound is short as in book.
2. The oo sound is long as in tooth.

1 Read each word under the picture and then write it on the lines below.

2 Read the sentences with your teacher. Underline the words that have the long oo sound as in tooth.

1. The baby got his first tooth when he was six months old.
2. We saw all the animals at the zoo.
3. It was such a cool day, we had to wear our coats.
4. Did you hear the cow moo?
5. The hoof on the horse was broken.
6. Dad had to fix the roof because there was a leak in it.
7. Cats like to play with a spool on a string.
8. The boys and girls had played so hard they had to snooze.
9. The rocks and stones were worn smooth.
10. It is fun to swim in a pool.

3 Circle the words your teacher reads.

1.	root	boost	moose
2.	shoot	boot	tooth
3.	zoo	school	stool
4.	spoon	spool	bloom

4 Read each word and then write it under the correct picture.

tooth roof moose root

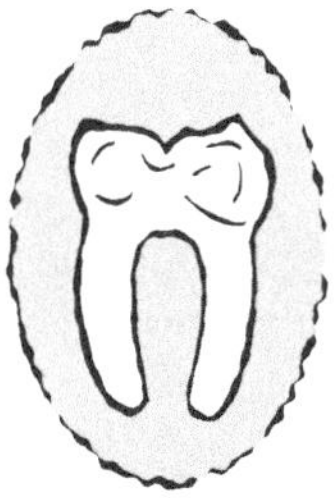

5 Print the sentence on the lines below.

I stay in a very good mood.

6 **Print the words from the word bank that rhyme.**

stoop noose boot moose toot droop

loose

root

coop

7 **Read the sentences with your teacher. From the word bank, print the vocabulary word that tells about the sentence.**

coop moose zoo food

1. Wild animals live in a nice place where people can see them.

2. Hens and roosters need a place to live and eat their food.

3. There is a wild animal with huge horns that can run very fast.

4. We need to eat the right things to stay healthy.

LESSON 137
Review: All Digraphs/Diphthongs

1 Spell the words under the pictures by choosing the correct digraph or diphthong sound. Choices: ay ey oy ow oo

2 Spell the words under the pictures by choosing the correct digraph or diphthong sound. Choices: aw au ey oi oy oo

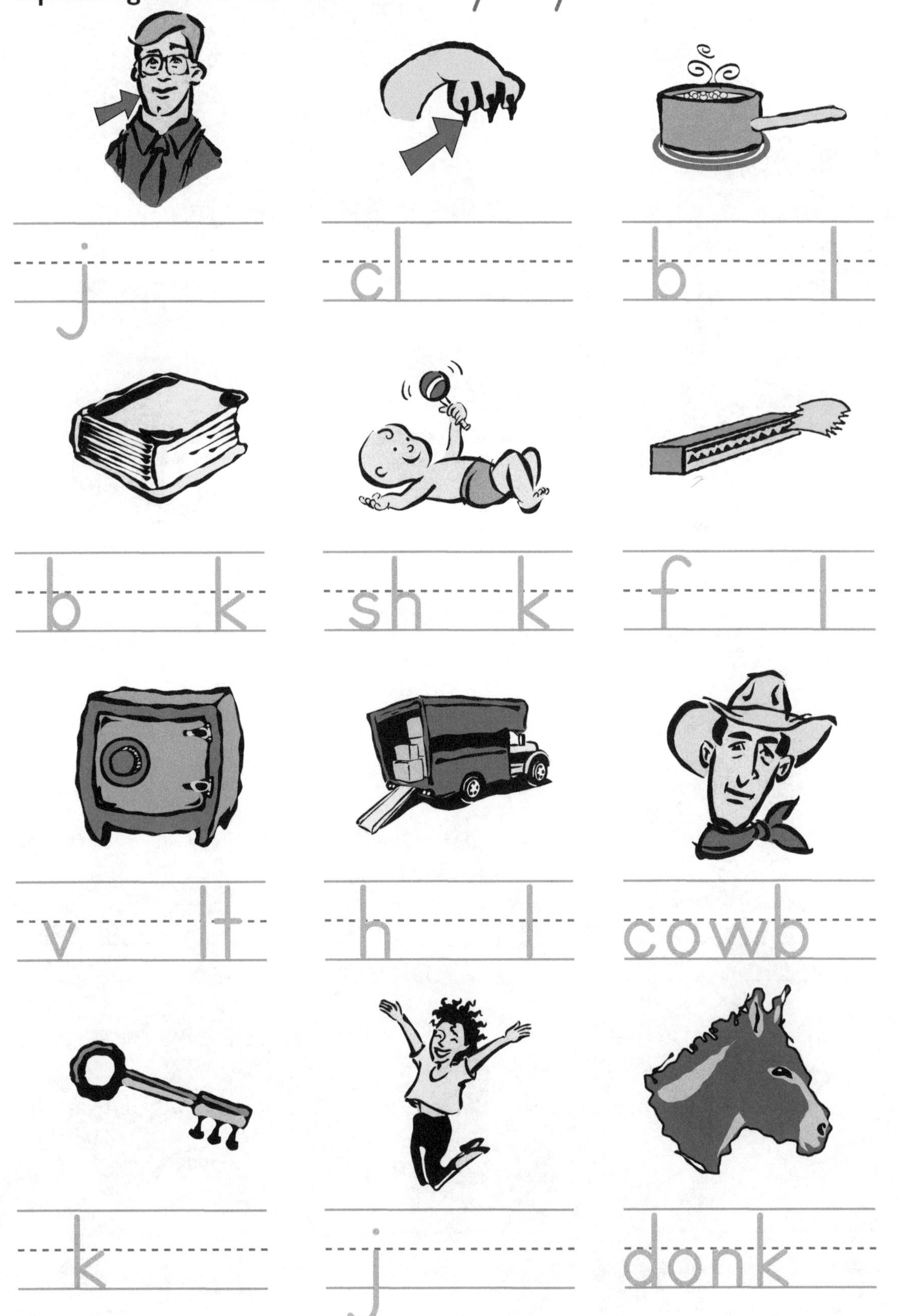

3 Spell the words under the pictures by choosing the correct digraph sound. Choices: ow oo ew

gr

m

h k

sm th

sl

cr

4 Circle the common nouns in each sentence that name a thing.

1. The claw of the bird is yellow.
2. Where did the boy go?
3. Jane had a blue shawl.
4. The vault is full of money.
5. Dad put a screw in the desk.

5 **Read the sentences below. Draw a line from the picture that matches the sentence.**

1. The monkey gave the tray to the clown.

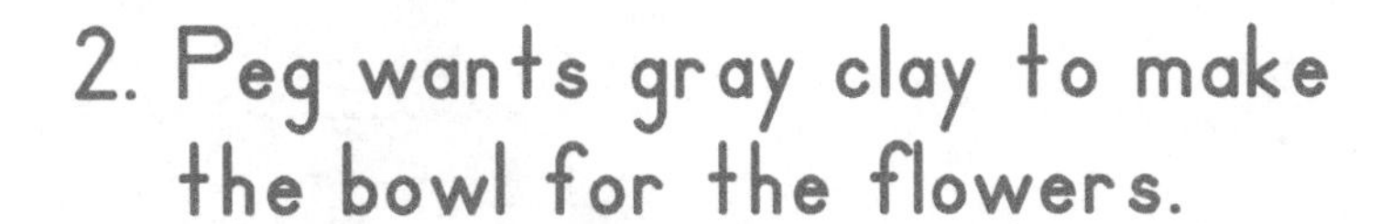

2. Peg wants gray clay to make the bowl for the flowers.

3. The donkey had a broken tooth in his jaw.

4. Drew took the book to school to show the other boys.

5. The cowboy took the rope out of the coil to catch the donkey.

6. The crew that will row the boat is in town.

LESSON 138

Review: Letter y; long i & e

1 Spell the words under the pictures by choosing the correct digraph or diphthong sound. Choices: y ay oy

fl

j

t

pr

tr

sk

2 Print the sentence using your name.

__________ is happy when reading a schoolbook.

3 Spell the words under the pictures by choosing the correct digraph or diphthong sound. Choices: oi ey ay

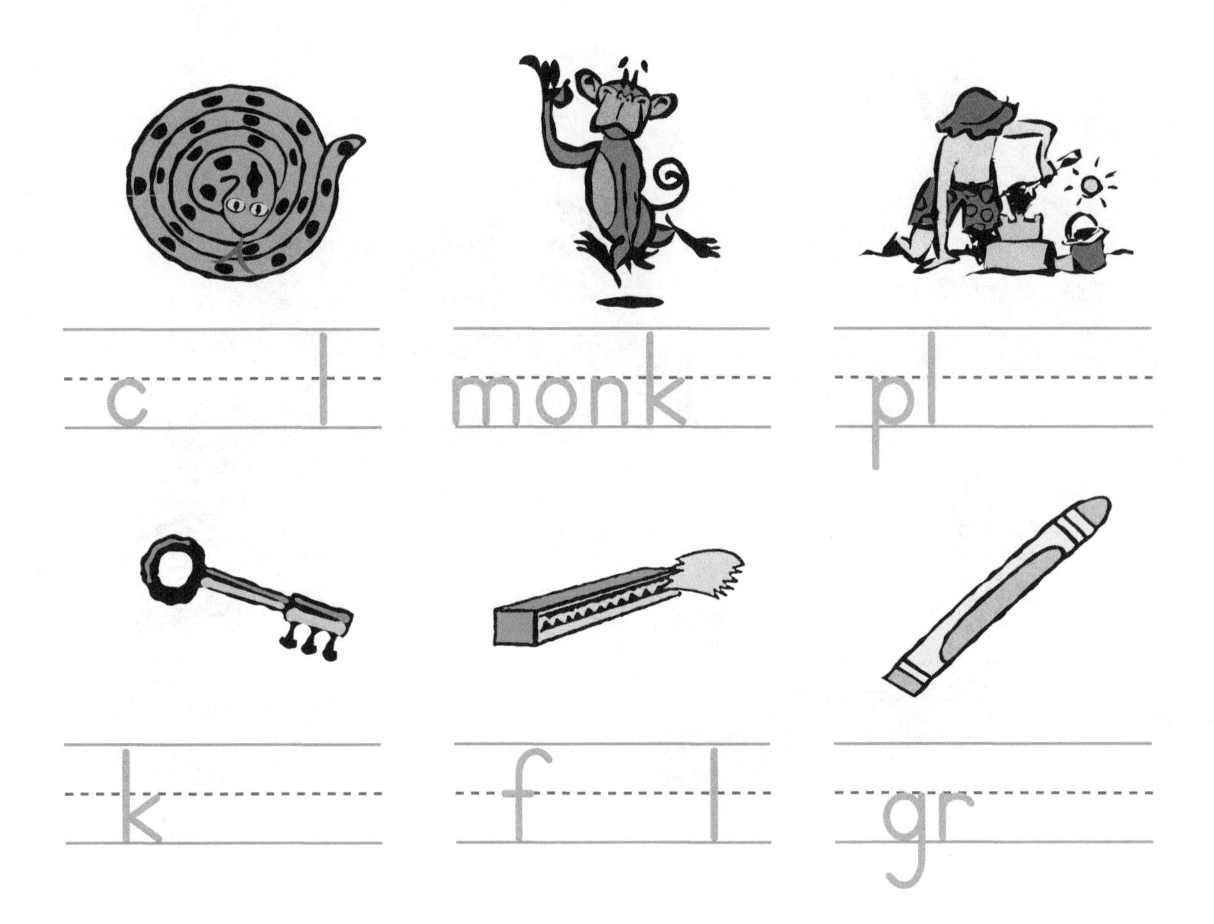

4 Circle the words your teacher reads.

1.	funny	baby	bunny
2.	enjoy	Troy	boy
3.	play	dandy	stay
4.	boil	broil	key
5.	foxy	fussy	tricky

5 Spell the words under the pictures by choosing the correct digraph or diphthong sound. Choices: y oy ay

6 Print the words from the word bank next to the word that rhymes.

handy	tray	coil	shady	monkey	coy

sandy ______ key ______

joy ______ toil ______

stay ______ lady ______

7 Choose and print the correct word to complete the sentence.

1. Dad will ______________ money so I can ride the horses. — tray / pay

2. Bobby keeps his ______________ in the trunk. — soy / toys

3. Donny will ______________ to lift the window. — try / dry

4. The ______________ lives in the zoo. — monkey / money

5. I hope you did not ______________ your dress when you fell. — foil / soil

6. We ate the ______________ that Mom gave us. — candy / caddy

LESSON 139
Silent Letter w

Rule: When w is followed by r, the w is silent, as in write.

1 Read each word under the picture and then write it on the line below.
Cross out the silent w.

wrench

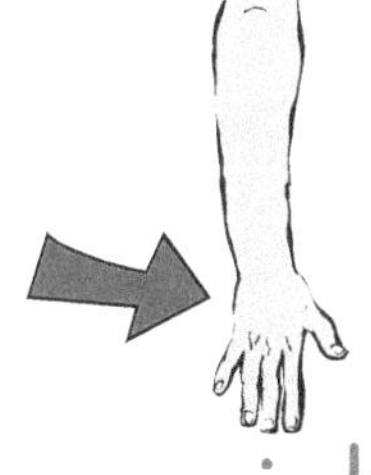
wrist

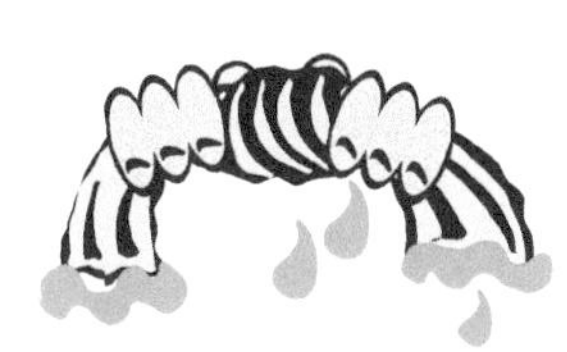
wring

wrinkle

writer

wrestler

2 Spell the correct word below each picture. Then print the rest of the words from the word bank on the lines below.

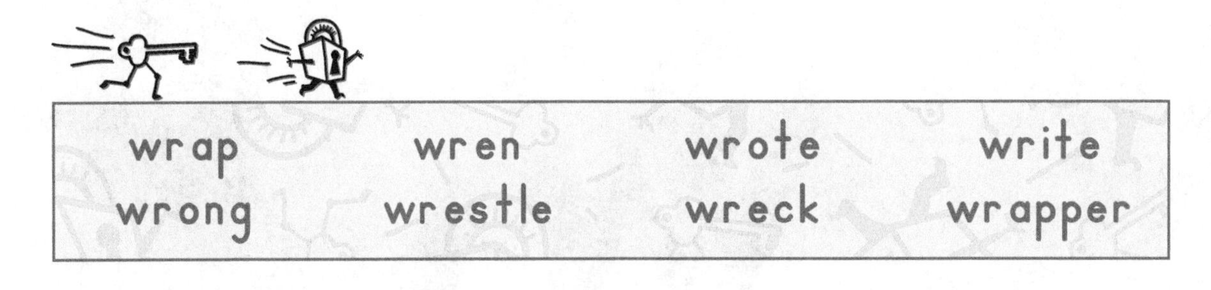

3 Look at the words below. When is the w silent? Draw a line under the words that have a silent w.

wrist write wood swift wrench wren

4 Read the sentences with your teacher. Underline the words that have a silent w at the beginning.

1. Dave will wrap the gift for his mom.
2. The wrestler has strong wrists.
3. Dad needed a wrench to fix his car.
4. The little wren had three eggs in her nest.
5. We saw two cars in a wreck.
6. I like to write a note to my pals.
7. The candy wrapper was in the trash.
8. At Christmas we put a wreath in the window.

5 Draw a line from the puzzle phrase to the picture it matches.

a wrestler with a wrench

a wreath on a wren

write with a wrench

two wrists on an arm

6 Look at the picture of a boy writing a letter. Tell your teacher two things about the picture. Then write a sentence of your own on the lines.

7 Circle the words your teacher reads.

wrestle	rest	fist	wrap	wrapper	trap
wrong	wrist	first	wren	hen	went
wreck	track	prank	wrist	test	tent

Silent k: knock

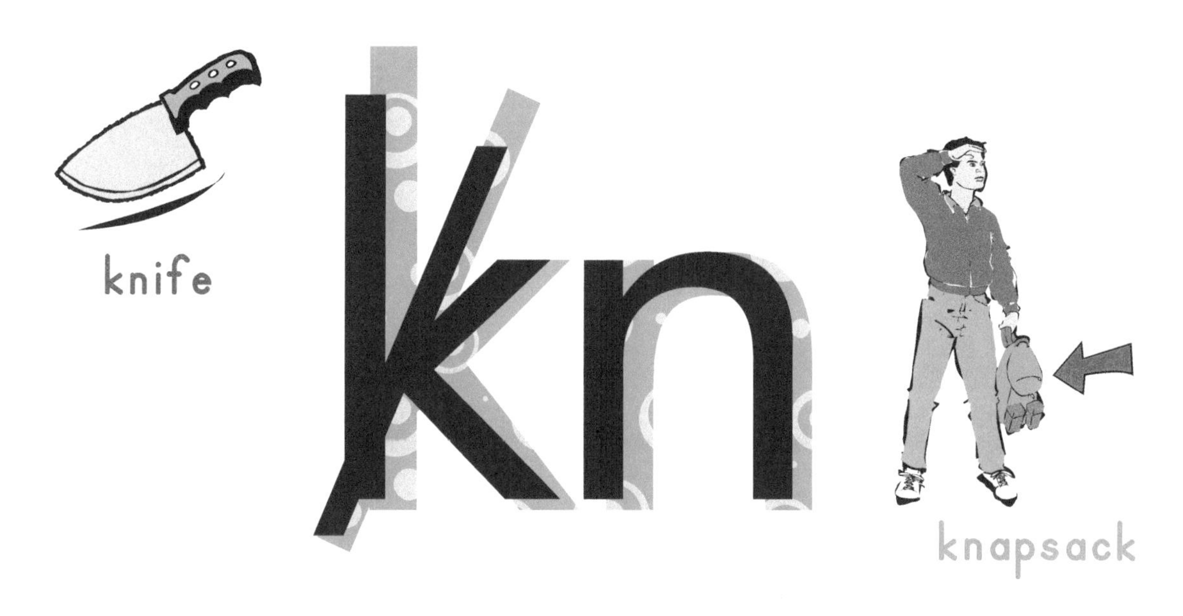

Rule: When k is followed by n the k is silent, as in knee.

1 Read each word under the picture and then write it on the line below. Cross out the silent k.

knock

knit

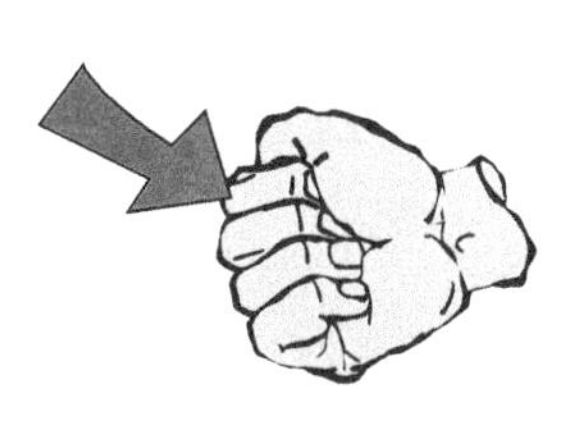

knuckle

knot

knee

knob

2 Spell the correct word from the word bank below each picture.

Then print the rest of the words on the lines below.

kneel	knot	knickers	knight
knob	knapsack	knock	knead

3 Draw a line from the puzzle phrase to the picture it matches.

a knee in a knot

knit a knapsack

knead with knuckles

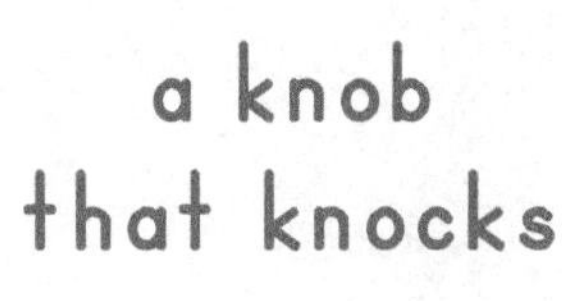

a knob that knocks

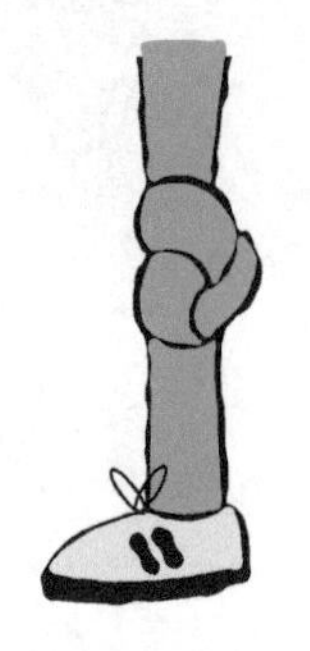

4 Read the sentences with your teacher. Underline the words that have a silent k at the beginning.

1. Can you tie knots in the string?
2. I knew that secret a long time ago.
3. Did you hear the knock at the door?
4. The knob on the front door will not work.
5. What will you put in your knapsack for camping?
6. My mom can knit a coat.
7. We cut the cake with a sharp knife.
8. People used to wear knickers for pants.
9. Jill got on her knees to say a prayer.
10. I know I like to read and write.

5 Circle the words your teacher reads.

1.	knob	knock	lock
2.	knit	kit	pink
3.	knuckle	buckle	kick
4.	knee	cheek	stream
5.	knot	knew	knife
6.	know	show	now

6 Look at the words below. When is the k silent? Draw a line under the words that have a silent k.

knife knit kitten kite knock

7 Look at the picture of a boy and girl on their knees in prayer. Tell your teacher two things about the picture. Then write a sentence of your own on the lines.

LESSON 141
Silent b: thumb

Rule: When mb is at the end of a word, the b is silent as in comb.

1 Read each word under the picture and then write it on the lines below. Cross out the silent b.

comb

bomb

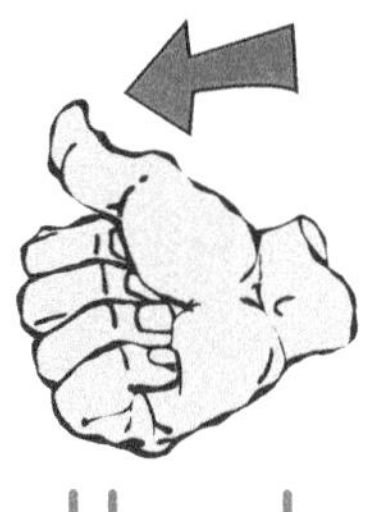

thumb

lamb

limb

climb

2 Spell the correct word below each picture. Then print the rest of the words on the lines below.

numb tomb climb bomb limb
plumb comb lamb crumb

3 Draw a line from the puzzle phrase to the picture it matches.

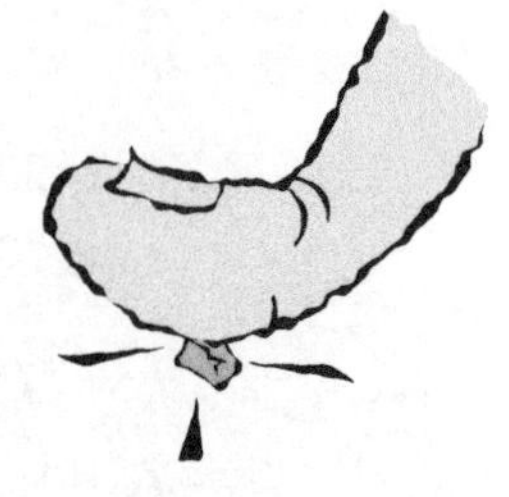

a lamb with a comb

a dumb thumb

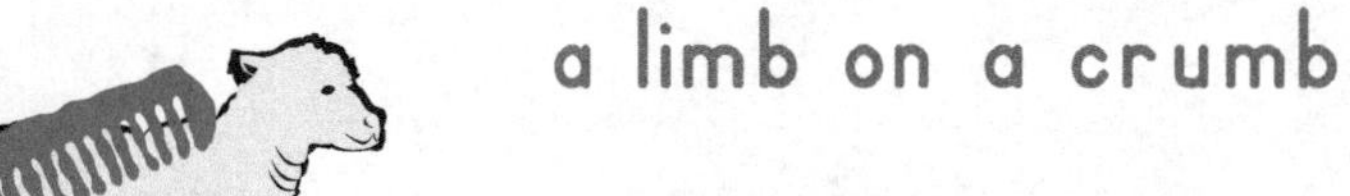
a limb on a crumb

a thumb crushing
a crumb

4 Circle the words your teacher reads.

1.	thumb	comb	wrist
2.	numb	wrinkle	knuckle
3.	lamb	numb	knit
4.	bomb	limb	write
5.	tomb	time	wren

5 Read the sentences with your teacher. Underline the words that have a silent b at the end.

1. The birds will eat all the crumbs.
2. My thumb is broken.
3. The man will plumb the kitchen sink.
4. The bomb will go off at seven.
5. She felt numb when she saw the bomb.
6. Can the baby climb the tree?
7. The baby lamb will be big next spring.
8. It is dumb to think you are dumb. You are smart.
9. Jan can fix her hair with her new comb.

6 Look at the words below. When is the b silent? Draw a line under the words that have a silent b.

thumb   stub   bulb   plumb   comb

7 Look at the picture of twin lambs playing in a park. The mother wants the twins to come home to the barn. Tell your teacher something about the picture. Then write a sentence of your own on the lines below.

LESSON 142
Review: Silent Letters b, k, w

1. Put a circle around the words that have a silent b.
2. Put a square around the words that have a silent k.
3. Underline the words that have a silent w.

knit	bomb	write	kite	baby	will
knife	wrong	blast	wrestler	comb	wrist
wring	knob	knot	wrap	climb	crumb

Draw a line from the word to the picture it matches. Then spell the word below each picture.

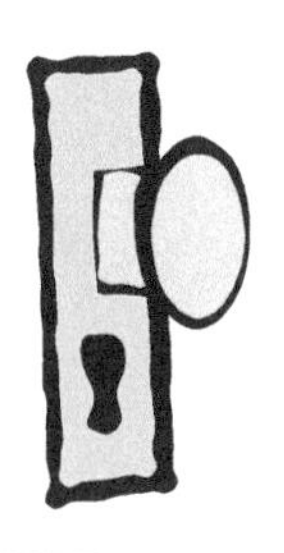

knob

comb

wrap

knit

write

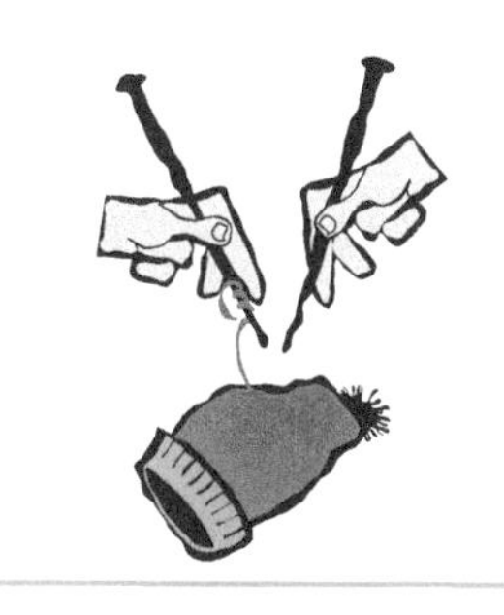

③ Circle the words your teacher reads.

1.	kitten	blast	bomb
2.	want	wrap	ship
3.	write	cowboy	broil
4.	king	kite	knife
5.	comb	joy	came
6.	knot	pry	play

④ 1. From the word bank, circle all the words that have a silent letter in them.

2. Print the words that you have circled on the lines below.

3. Put a line through the silent letter in each of words you have printed.

climb	silk	wrist	best	know
kneel	comb	will	wrote	frank

5 Read the sentences. Draw a line to the picture that matches the sentence.

1. We will write a note to say thank you for the party.

2. Mom had to use a knife to fix the peaches for the pie.

3. The noise was so loud it sounded like a bomb.

4. The wrestler came to town to show his skills.

5. I will wrap the gift for my mom.

6. Men used to wear knickers instead of pants.

7. Did you comb your hair a new way?

6 Look at the picture. It tells about Nan getting a letter from Jane. In the letter Jane asked Nan to come to her house for her sixth birthday party. Nan is happy. She wants to go. Read the note with your teacher.

Dear Nan,

I will be six years old on Monday, June 14th. I would like to have you come to my party at 2:00 P.M. The party will be held at my house. Please let me know if you would like to come.

Your friend,

Jane

7 Talk with your teacher about how you can send a note to Jane telling her that you would like to go to the party. Print it on the lines below.

Dear ,

Your friend,

8 Draw a picture of Jane's birthday party.

LESSON 143
Silent Letter g

Rule: When the letter g is followed by the letter n in a word, the g is silent as in gnat.

1 Read each word under the picture and then write it on the lines below. Cross out the silent g.

gnash

gnu

gnat

gnaw

sign

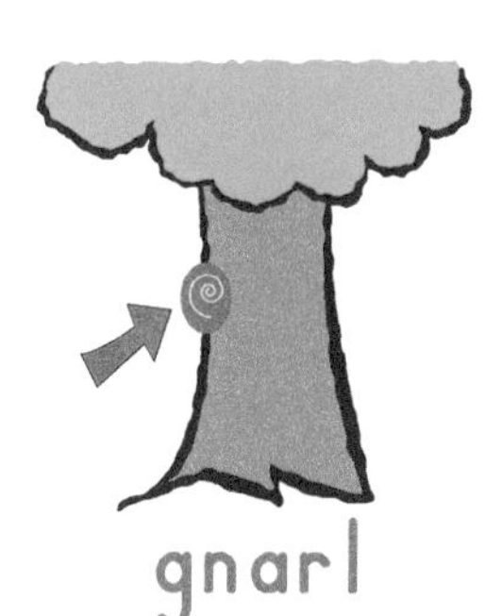

gnarl

2 Spell the correct word below each picture. Then print the rest of the words on the lines below

3 Circle the words your teacher reads.

1.	sign	sing	ring
2.	write	comb	gnash
3.	gnat	get	knee
4.	gnaw	keep	numb

4 Read the sentences. Underline the words that have a silent gn in them. Draw a line from the sentence to the picture it matches.

1. A gnat is an insect that can bite and sting.

2. The shark looked like he would gnash his teeth.

3. Spot, the dog, will gnaw on any bone he finds.

4. A gnu has horns and a head like an ox.

5. A gnarl is a hard knot on the trunk of a tree.

6. Dad must stop his car when he sees a stop sign.

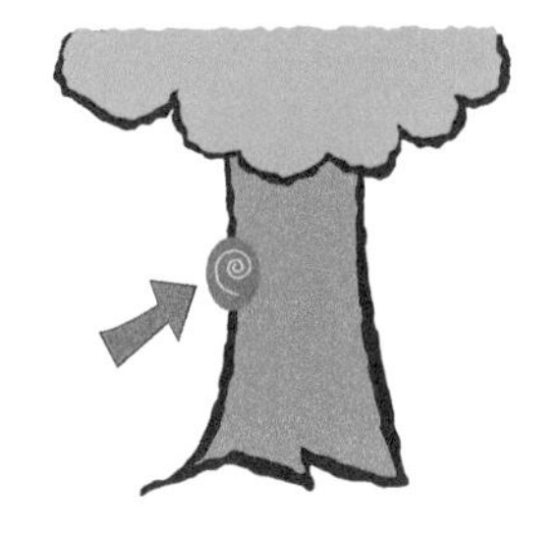

5 Look at the words below in the word bank.

1. Circle all the words that have a silent letter in them.
2. Print the words that you have circled on the lines below.
3. Put a line through the silent letter in each of the words you have printed.

comb	wring	knit	knee	sing	lamb	wrestle
sign	gnat	wish	climb	gnarl	gnu	plumb

6 Look at the picture where Mike is at the swimming pool. He is diving from the side of the pool. Talk to your teacher about Mike's safety. Ask some of these questions.

no lifeguard on duty

no diving

no running

1. Does Mike have someone with him?
2. Is the water too deep?
3. Does Mike know how to swim?
4. Did he read all of the signs?

7 Think of another question that could be asked. Have your teacher help you print it on the lines below. Be sure to put a capital letter on the first word and a question mark at the end.

8 Draw a picture.

Rule: When the letter i comes before gh or ght, the i is long, and gh is silent.

1 Read the words under the pictures.

1. Put a circle around the pictures that have a silent gh.
2. Cross out the silent letters gh in each word you circle.

2 Finish spelling the word under each picture by filling in the beginning and ending letters.

3 Finish spelling the word under each picture by filling in the middle letters in the word.

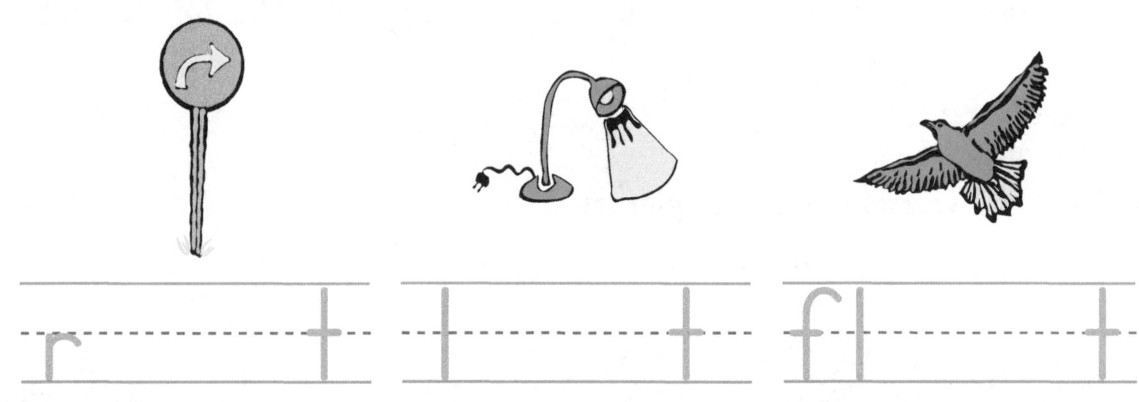

4 Draw a line from the phrase to the picture it matches.

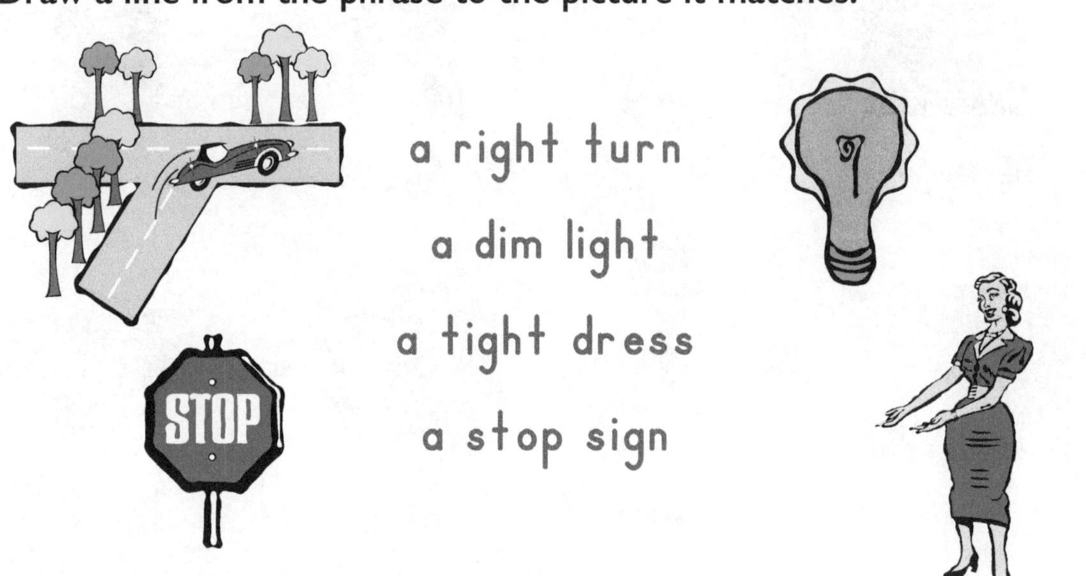

5 Read the sentences with your teacher.

1. Draw a line under the sentence that matches the picture.

2. Print the correct sentence on the lines below.

It is too late at night to take a ride.
It is too late at right to take a ride.

Please stop at the gnat sign.
Please stop at the stop sign.

STOP

The wrestlers had a fight in the ring.
The wrestlers had a light in the wrong.

6 Circle the word your teacher reads.

1.	flight	flat	fight
2.	sign	sight	stop
3.	right	wrong	gnat
4.	light	lamp	look

7 Look at the picture below. There are two things that use the ight words you have had in this lesson. Put a circle around those two things and print the words on the lines below.

LESSON 145
Review: Silent Letters w, k, b, gn, gh

1. Read the word under the pictures. Underline the silent letter(s) in each word.

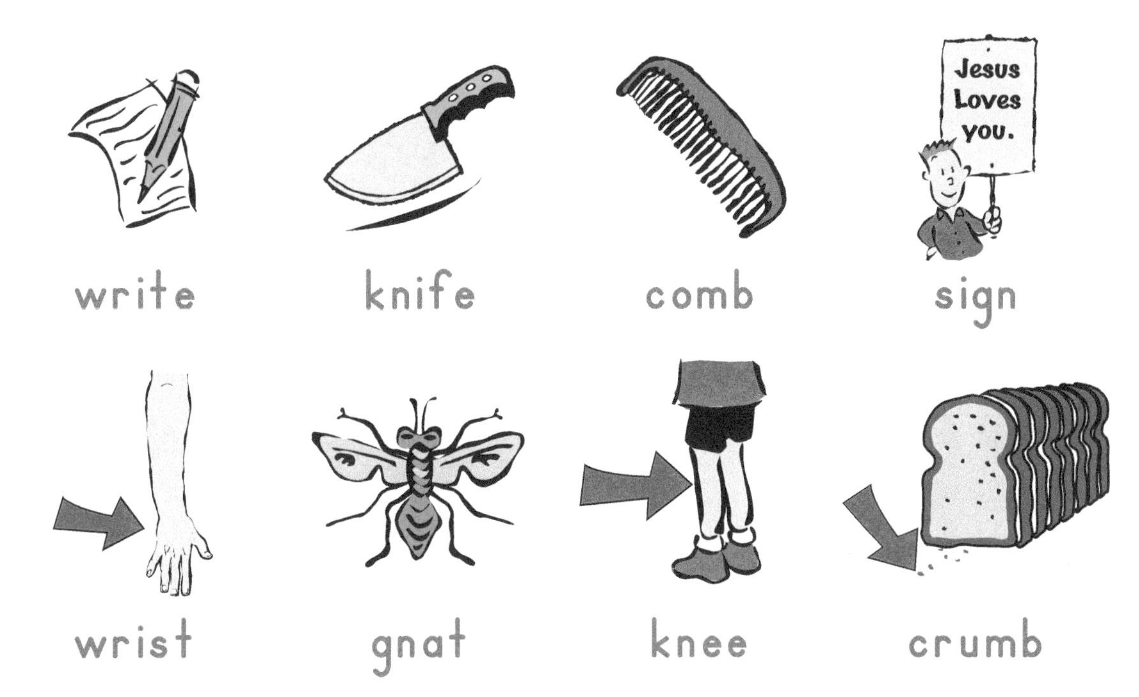

write	knife	comb	sign
wrist	gnat	knee	crumb

2. Read the words. Underline the silent letter(s) in each word.

1.	knee	knuckle	knit
2.	wrist	wrinkle	wrong
3.	slight	night	sight
4.	comb	thumb	numb

3 Print the words in rows.

Silent g

Silent gh

Silent k

Silent b

Silent w

4 Read the story. Then answer the questions.

Wesley is five years old. He has just started school. Wesley has a pen in his knapsack. He has a book about a wrestler. He wants to learn to read and write.

1. How old is Wesley?

five
six
seven

2. What did he have in his knapsack?

rocks
cap
pen

3. What person was in his storybook?

driver
wrestler
mother

4. What did Wesley want to learn to do at school?

read and write
sing and spell
play and jump

5 Talk to your teacher about what you want most when you are in school. Print a sentence about that on the lines below.

6 Circle the word your teacher reads.

1.	written	knife	wrestle
2.	wrap	kitten	knot
3.	thumb	light	sign
4.	knuckle	lamb	wrinkle
5.	gnaw	keep	flight

When a word ends with the letters le,
it makes the sound of ul, as in saddle.

1 Read the word under each picture and then write it on the line below.

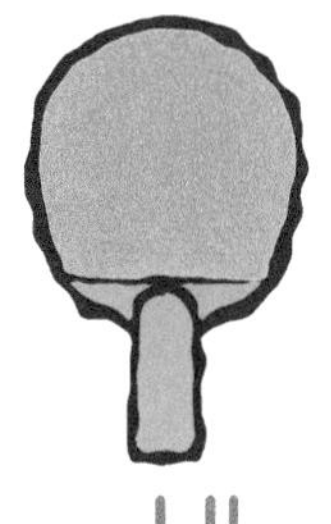
paddle

candle

bottle

people

kettle

apple

2 Read the word under each picture and then write it on the line below.

3 Draw a line from the word to the picture it matches. Spell the word below the picture.

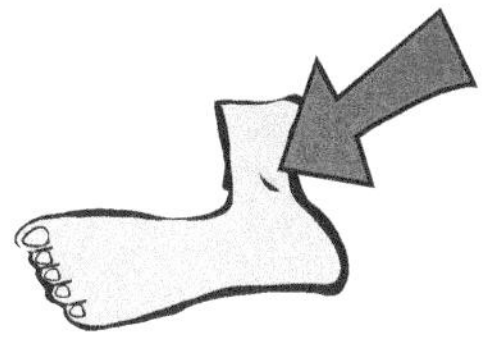

cattle

bottle

people

candle

thimble

ankle

puddle

jungle

4 Draw a line from the puzzle phrase to the picture.

cattle in
a puddle

a candle
on an apple

a saddle
on a person

a rattle
on her ankle

5 Read the sentences. Underline the words that end with the letters le.

1. My uncle asked us a riddle.
2. Did you get the new fishing tackle?
3. The dogs played in a puddle of water.
4. Jack has some little kittens that wiggle all over.
5. We have a kettle on our table.
6. Dave's horse has a new saddle.

6 **Print the word from the word bank that completes the sentence.**

grumble	tumble	kettle	thimble	saddle	middle

Some people can ride horses better if they have a ________ .

A ________ is used to cook food or boil water.

You could take a ________ over a stick and fall down.

If someone fusses about something, we think she will ________ .

The center of something can be the ________ .

A ________ is useful to put on the middle finger when sewing.

7 **Read the story. Then answer the questions.**

When Sam was seven years old, his dad got him a saddle horse to ride. Sam named the horse Shorty. Sam got on the horse and away they trotted down the road. The horse stumbled over a pile of rocks and pebbles. Sam fell off and landed in a puddle.

1. Where did Sam get his horse?

from the store
from his dad
from the ranch

2. What did Sam name his horse?

Ned
Spotty
Shorty

3. Where did the horse start to go?

down the road
to the barn
to town

4. What happened to the horse?

bucked
stumbled
walked home

5. What happened to Sam?

fell into a puddle
broke his leg
walked away

LESSON 147
Words With all

Words with all in them have the sound we hear in the word ball.

1 Read the word under each picture. Then print it on the line below.

2 Draw a line from the word to the picture it matches. Spell the word under each picture.

3 Read the sentences. Underline the words that have all in them.

1. Did Jake catch the ball when it came over the house?
2. Jane is as tall as her sister.
3. I hope Mom will call me so I can get to school on time.
4. The little girl cannot draw on the white wall.
5. Bert went to the mall to shop.
6. Jim ran to first base when he played baseball.
7. Dave has a new football.

4 Draw a line from the puzzle phrase to the picture it matches.

a fish with a ball

a tall ant

the sky will fall

a small elephant
with a football

5 Choose the word from the word bank that completes the sentence.

wall	baseball	rainfall	tall	football

1. Someone who is not short is ______________.

2. We hung a chart on the ______________ of the school.

3. Bob went to first base when he was playing ______________.

4. We got wet from the ______________.

5. Dave got to the goal line when he played ______________.

6 Read the story. Then answer the questions.

Beth and Jane went with Dad to the pool to swim. Jane was running and fell into the pool at the deep end. Beth had to call Dad for help. Dad jumped in the pool to help Jane.

1. Where did Beth and Jane go?

to the pool
to the park
to the zoo

2. What happened to Jane?

she got hurt
she fell
she jumped

3. What did Beth have to do?

yell loud
run away
call Dad

4. Who came to help?

a stranger
her dad
her teacher

7 Talk to your teacher about the safety rules when you swim. Print a sentence that tells about safety and swimming.

LESSON 148
Syllables

A syllable is a part of a word spoken as a sound group.
A syllable can be divided between double consonants,
as in kit·ten, or between two consonants, as in can·dy.

1. Put a circle around the words under the pictures that have two syllables with double consonants in the middle.

2. Put a square around the words under the pictures that have two syllables divided by two different consonants.

3 Draw a line from the word to the picture it matches.

ribbon

window

valley

candy

cotton

number

donkey

bottom

picnic

4 Practice printing words with a double consonant or two different consonants in the middle.

rabbit funny basket doctor

5 Read the sentences. Underline the words that have double consonants in the middle.

1. The rabbit hopped on the grass.
2. Daddy took us to the lake last summer.
3. The car drove by the tunnel near the main road.
4. The cattle were in the barn eating hay.
5. The baby had to have help with the button on his coat.

6 Put the words in alphabetical order.

cotton button tunnel apple

1. ______________ 3. ______________

2. ______________ 4. ______________

7 Spell the correct word below each picture. Then print the rest of the words on the lines below.

8 Complete the sentence that describes the picture. Print the word from the word bank in the space.

paddle	bottle	dollar	puddle	apple	ruffle

1. Some people drink from a _______________, but others want a cup.

2. A _______________ can be used to row a boat.

3. When he fell in a mud _______________ he got dirty.

4. This red _______________ grows on a tree and is good to eat.

5. The girl has a _______________ on her dress.

6. Ten dimes make one _______________.

9 Read the story. Then answer the questions. Print the answers to the first three questions on the lines below. Talk about question number four.

Billy got a new bike for his birthday. He rode it around the lake all day. When he got home, he forgot to put the bike away in the shed. That night the bike was stolen.

1. When did Billy get his bike?

2. Where did he ride the bike?

3. What happened to the bike?

4. What should Billy have done?

LESSON 149
Syllables: Compound Words

Compound words are made by combining two words into one. Example: cowboy.

1 Put a circle around each base word in the compound words below.

2 Draw a line between the two words that make up the compound word in the word bank below.

blacksmith	upset	lifejacket	lighthouse	eyeball
notebook	downpour	herself	without	snowman

light	self	with	book
her	smith	life	ball
up	pour	note	man
down	set	eye	jacket
black	house	snow	out

3 Look at the words under each picture below. Put them together to make a compound word. Print the compound word on the lines below.

foot ball

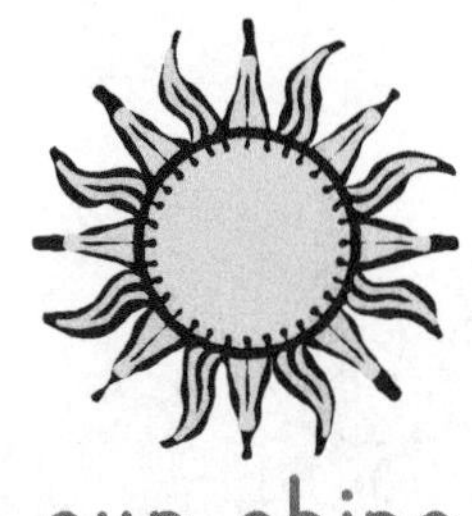

sun shine

sales man

air port

grass hopper

up stairs

4 Look at the words below. Circle all the words that have double consonants in the middle. Put a square around the compound words.

herself ribbon anyone bookcase barefoot

northwest kitten little lifejacket pigtail

5 Read the sentences. Put a circle around the compound word(s) in the sentence.

1. We can go to the lake anyway.
2. There was a downpour of rain.
3. I do not want to go without you.
4. The jet flew into the airport at three in the afternoon.
5. The fisherman got four catfish when he was at the lake.
6. We had a fun trip on the houseboat.
7. We saw the truck when it had a blowout of its tire.
8. Don plays shortstop with the baseball team.

6 In your own words, tell your teacher what each of the compound words mean.

1. baseball
2. barefoot
3. rowboat
4. upstairs
5. classmate

7 Draw a line from the puzzle phrase to the picture it matches.

a catfish with
a horseshoe

a kickstand
on a truck

a football
with a hat

a donkey on
a runway

a cat on a
flagpole

a snowman
on a houseboat

LESSON 150
Syllables: Consonant Between Vowels

Rule: A single consonant between vowels usually goes with the second vowel. Example: ti·ger, wa·ter

1. Put a circle around the words under the pictures that have two syllables.

spider girl police hotel

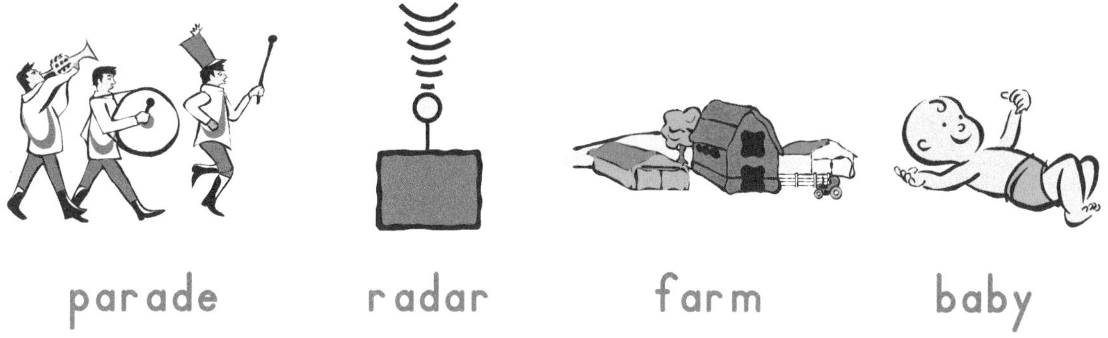

parade radar farm baby

vacant alone tame pirate

2 Look at the word bank. Choose and print the word below the picture it matches. Underline the one consonant between the vowels and show that it goes with the second syllable.

3 Put a circle around the words your teacher reads.

1.	tiger	trees	trade
2.	spider	safe	sift
3.	pirate	pain	pick
4.	radar	roof	rain

4 Draw a line from the puzzle phrase to the picture it matches.

a pig with
a basket

a spider in
a pocket

a pirate in pain

a tiger with
a dentist

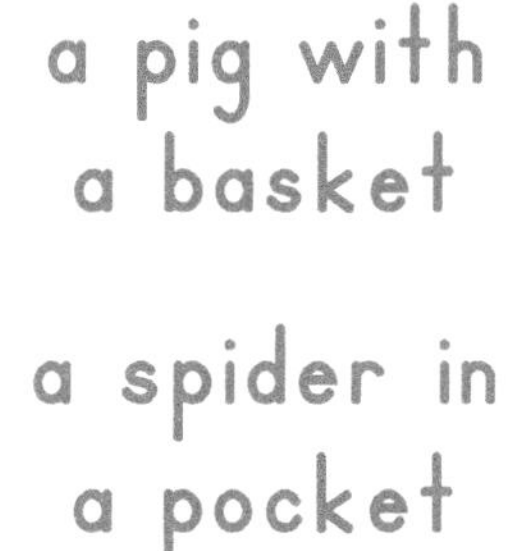

5 Read the sentences. Underline the words that have two syllables.

1. The pilot met us at the airport.
2. How many teeth does a tiger have?
3. How many legs does a spider have?
4. Ron put the eggs in a basket.
5. The water is frozen in the pond.
6. Dad used lumber to make a shed.

6 Look at the pictures. Print 1 under the one that happens first, 2 under the next one, and 3 under the one that would happen last.

7 Print the sentences below. Be sure to use a capital letter at the beginning and a period or a question mark at the end.

janet will go to the dentist

will you see a tiger at the zoo

LESSON 151
Review: All Syllables

1. Put a circle around the compound words under the pictures.

basketball

candy

aircraft

pocket

ponytail

mailbox

basket

baseball

2. Put a square around the two-syllable words that are not compound words.

airport

window

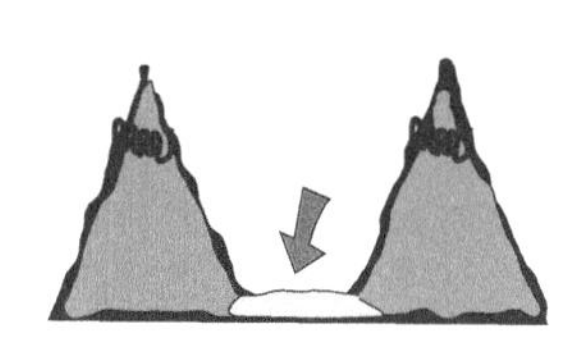
valley

grasshopper

bottom

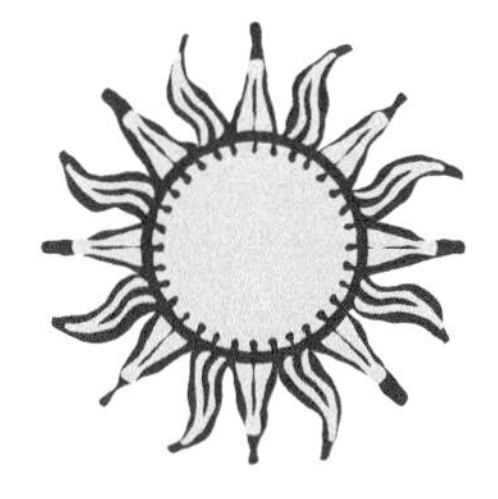
sunshine

picnic

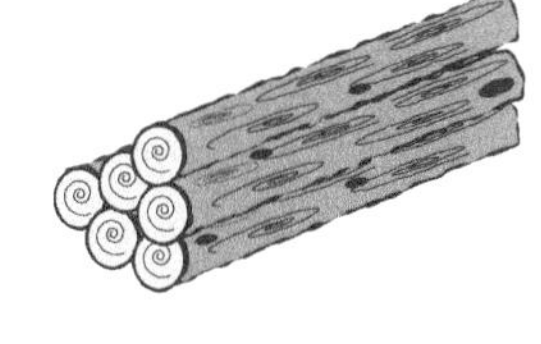
lumber

3. Underline the two-syllable words that have a single consonant between the vowels.

tiger summer hotel rattle

pocket water bubble spider

4. Draw a line from the word to the picture it matches.

baseball

rowboat

beehive

rattle

football

birthday

LESSON 151
Review: All Syllables

5 Choose and print the correct word on the lines in each sentence.

1. The ______________ are in the barnyard. — collar / cattle

2. Janet put the eggs in a ______________ on the table. — basket / barrel

3. Jack put a ______________ on the horse so he could lead it. — bridle / bottle

4. The monkey lived in a ______________ . — number / jungle

5. The little rocks looked like ______________ . — pebbles / wiggles

6 Think of some compound words you know. Talk to your teacher and use a sheet of paper to print a sentence of your own using a compound word.

7 Think of some words that have a double consonant in the middle. Talk to your teacher and print your own sentence on a sheet of paper.

8 Look at the words in the word bank. Choose and print a word on the line that would make the sentence correct.

dollar	doctor	tigers	bottle
lumber	football	buttons	

1. The money that is the same as ten dimes is a ________.

2. Houses are often made of ________.

3. When you are sick, you see a ________.

4. Baby Jane drinks her milk from a ________.

5. Most people like to watch a good ________ game.

6. When we go to the zoo, we like to see the ________.

7. A shirt often has six ________.

LESSON 152
Suffix ing

Suffixes are word segments at the end of a word.

It can change or add meaning to the base word.

Example: boss - bossing; sell - selling

1 **Read the word under each picture. Then print it on the lines below.**

fixing

buzzing

bucking

yelling

camping

kissing

2 **Draw a line from the word to the picture it matches. Spell the word below the picture.**

docking

bunking

asking

dusting

mixing

fishing

bending

dumping

3 **Fill in the blank spaces in each base word with** ing**. Read the sentence and underline the base word.**

1. My dad is fix ______ the roof on the house.

2. Jan is look ______ at the money in her bank.

3. The gang is yell ______ at the football game.

4. We will go fish ______ at the lake.

5. The lady is sell ______ rings at the store.

6. All the kids are duck ______ under the bar.

7. Two cars were bump ______ into each other.

8. The man with the cane was limp ______.

9. We set up the tent when we went camp ______.

A preposition is a word that connects parts of the sentence, such as in the house, by the stove, and from the girl.

4 Look at the pictures. Draw a line to the prepositional phrase that tells about the picture.

The fish were

under the fishbowl.
in the fishbowl.
behind the fishbowl.

Three books were

behind other books.
under the table.
on the shelf.

Sam sat

in the chair.
under the desk.
on the swing.

Mom fixed dinner

for the family.
with all the ladies.
at six o'clock.

5 **Look at the pictures below. Underline the preposition that connects the sentence.**

The boy sits on a chair.

My dog puts his bone in the dirt.

Jan has her feet under the table.

Did you look for your toy behind the couch?

6 **Look at the pictures below. Underline the preposition that connects the sentence.**

The bird's nest is inside the birdhouse.

The cat's tail is curved around his neck.

Mom will fix dinner for six people.

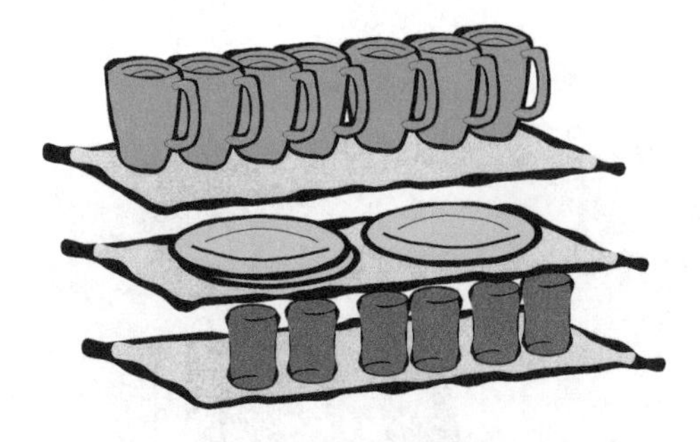

We put the mugs above the middle shelf.

LESSON 153
Special Soft c

iceberg

ocelot

Rule: When c is followed by e, i, or y, the c is called soft and makes the sound of sss. Example: city, cent, cycle, face

1 Read the word under each picture and then print it on the line below.

ace

ice

center

pencil

fence

city

2 Draw a line from the word to the picture it matches. Spell the word below the picture.

3 Talk to your teacher about the nouns that are persons, places or things. Print two nouns for each.

Persons	Places	Things

4 Read the sentences below. Underline the word(s) in each sentence that has the soft c sound.

1. Fran drove to the city in her new car.
2. We will have a race to the fence.
3. Did you draw a circle on your paper?
4. I have an ace of spades in my hand.
5. Mom fixed rice for dinner.
6. The road was icy from the frost.

5 Look at the words in the word bank. Use one of the words to complete the sentence.

price	mice	space	dance

1. An airplane takes up a lot of ________.
2. The ________ of the car was too much to pay.
3. There were three baby ________ in a cage.
4. The music was so good I wanted to ________.

6 Read the words that have the soft c in them. Choose six of the words below to practice.

race	grace	face	place	lace
nice	spicy	fancy	fence	cedar
celery	circus	city	twice	dance

Review: A noun is the name of a person, place or thing.

7 Underline the nouns in each sentence. Count the number of nouns and write it in the space at the end of the sentence.

1. Bob took his horses to the barn. ________
2. Beth went to town to see a show. ________
3. The fish were swimming in the pond. ________
4. Bill wants to go home. ________
5. Dad cooked dinner. ________

LESSON 154
Special Soft g

magic

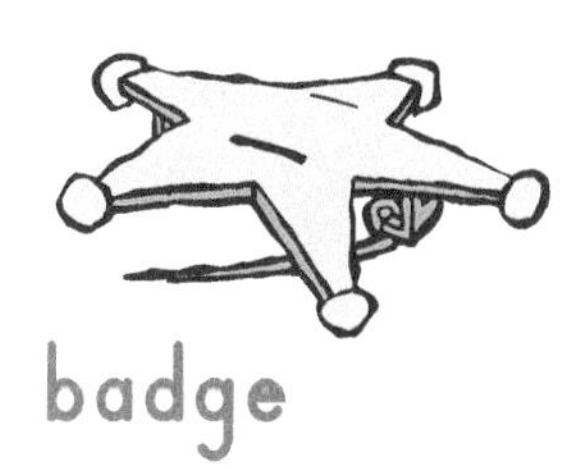

badge

Rule: When g is followed by e, i, or y, the g is called soft g and makes the sound of j. Example: cage, giant

1 Read the word under each picture and then print it on the line below.

gem

dodge

large

giant

judge

range

2 Draw a line from the word to the picture it matches. Finish spelling the word below the picture by filling in the dge.

3. Draw a line from the word to the picture it matches. Finish spelling the word below the picture by filling in the g in the middle of the word.

gadget

Ginger

fidget

magic

gad_et

Gin_er

ma_ic

fid_et

4. Put the words in alphabetical order.

giraffe land basket comb

1. ________

2. ________

3. ________

4. ________

5 Look at the words in the word bank below. Print the words in the correct columns below.

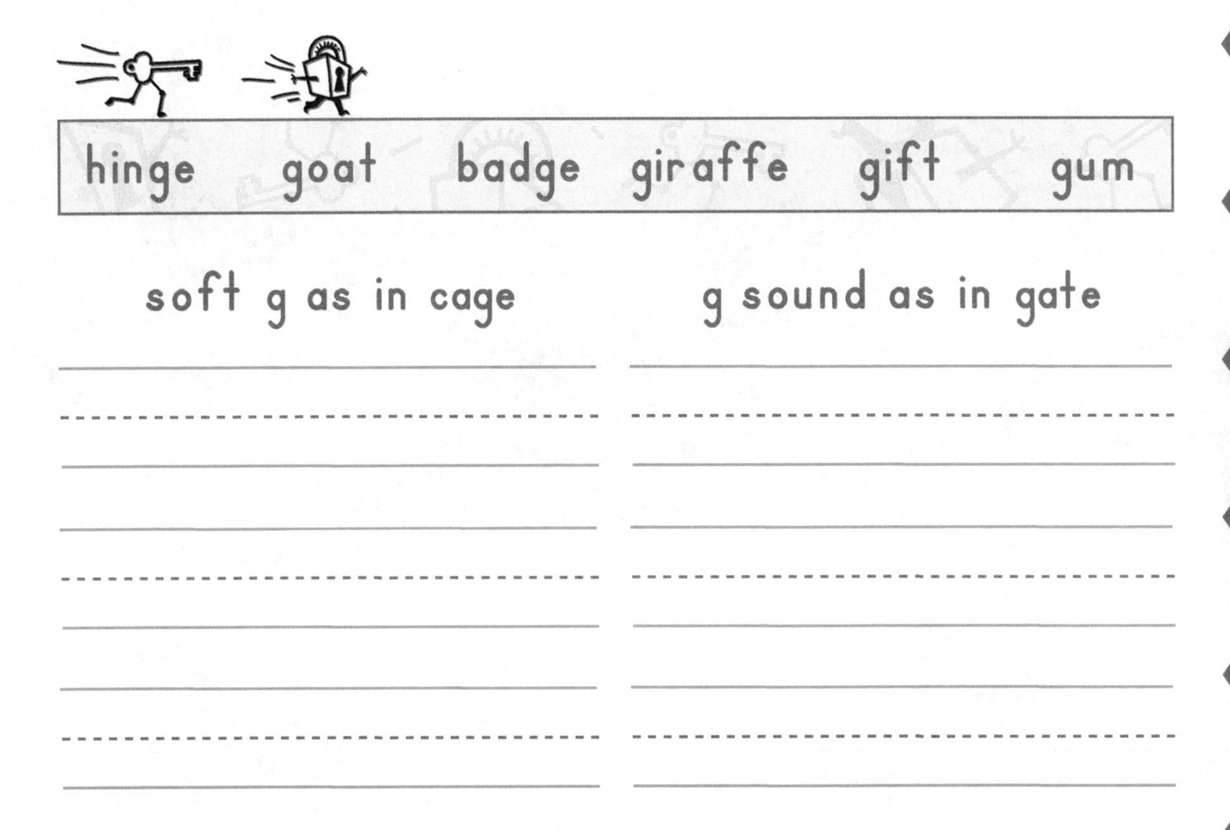

hinge goat badge giraffe gift gum

soft g as in cage	g sound as in gate

6 Read the sentences below. Underline the word(s) in each sentence that has the soft g sound.

1. Will Ginger manage when her mom is not at home?
2. We put the car on a huge barge.
3. The farmer had cattle on the range.
4. The school went to the zoo to see the giraffe.
5. Gene was on the stage at school.

LESSON 155
Review: Ending ing; Soft c, g

1 Read the base words in the word bank. Print the words below by adding ing to them. Underline the base word.

camp	bend	fix	sell
add	box	cast	catch

camp fix

add cast

bend sell

box catch

2. From the words in the word bank, choose and print the word to make the sentence correct.

filling	chilling	dumping	brushing	blasting	spilling

1. The baby was ______________ his milk all over his crib.

2. We can hear the ______________ of the bomb.

3. Meg keeps ______________ her hair so it stays nice.

4. Mom was ______________ the pudding so it would stay cool.

5. The truck will be ______________ the trash all day.

6. Is Janet ______________ the glass too full of milk?

3 Soft c review. Sometimes c sounds like s. Circle the correct word in each box that names the picture.

cash celery	candy circle	city cot	cent camel

4 From the words in the word bank, choose and print the word to make the sentence correct.

celery	cents	dance	circus	city

1. Five ______________ is the same as a nickel.

2. I like to eat ______________ with my dinner.

3. The ______________ animals were eating their food.

4. I hope we do not have to move to a big ______________.

5. Marge had a nice dress for the ______________.

5. Soft g review. Sometimes g sounds like j. Circle the correct word in each box that names the picture.

giraffe glass	bank badge	gum giant	gem goat

6. From the words in the word bank, choose and print the word to make the sentence correct.

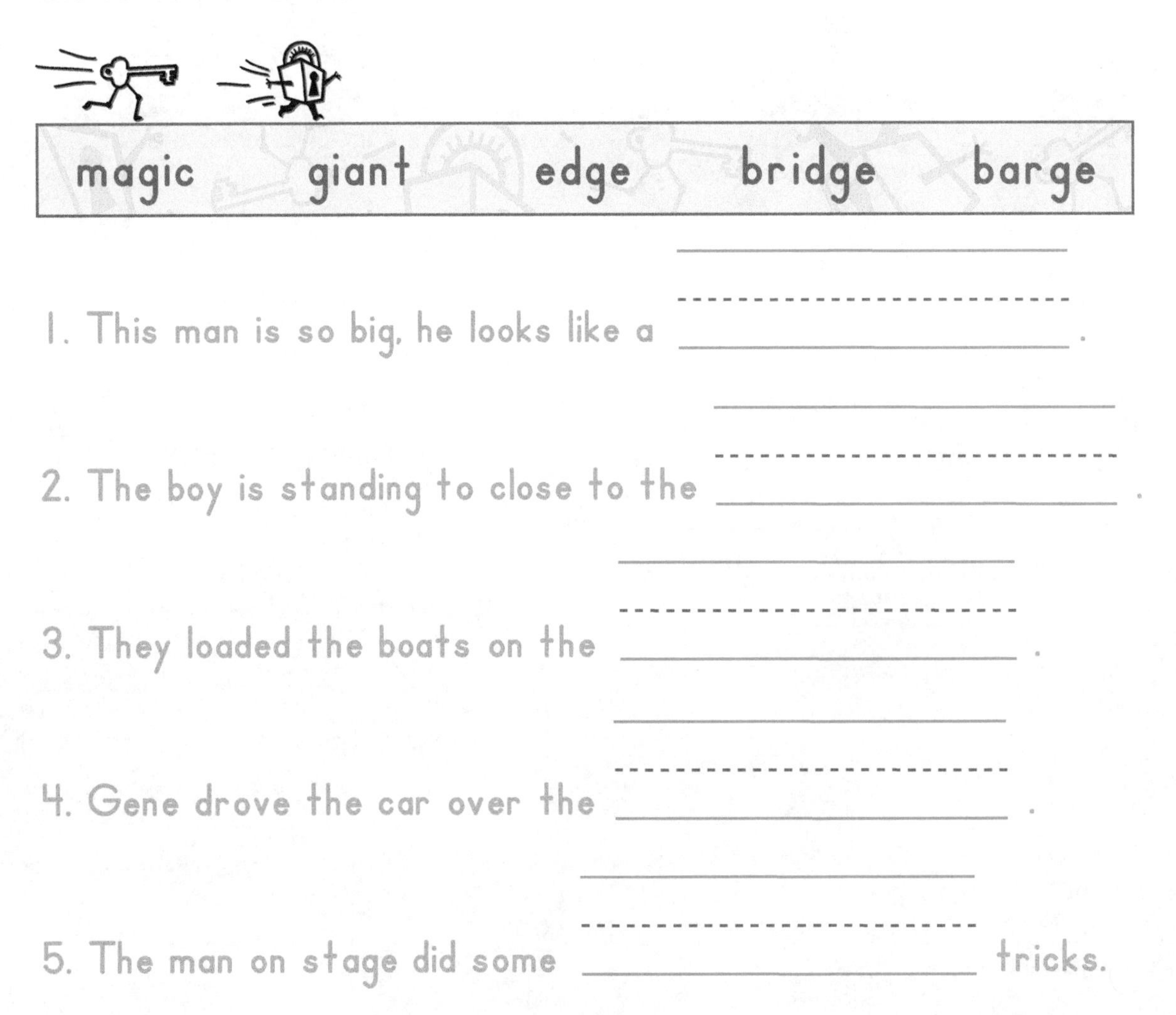

magic	giant	edge	bridge	barge

1. This man is so big, he looks like a ______________.

2. The boy is standing to close to the ______________.

3. They loaded the boats on the ______________.

4. Gene drove the car over the ______________.

5. The man on stage did some ______________ tricks.

7 Look at all three pictures in the mini story. Read the sentences. Put a 1 on the line under the picture that should come first in the story. Put 2 under the picture that comes next, and 3 under the picture that would be last in the story.

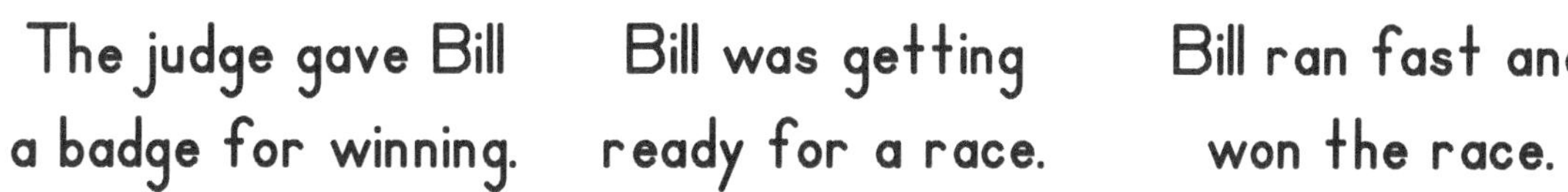

The judge gave Bill a badge for winning.

Bill was getting ready for a race.

Bill ran fast and won the race.

8 Look at the pictures. Put 1 under the picture that happens first, 2 under the next one, and 3 under the one that would happen last.

9 Draw a line from the puzzle phrase to the picture it matches.

a giant
in a rage

a gypsy
in a cage

a badge on
a giraffe

a gerbil
with a goose

10 Look at the table with food on it. Talk to your teacher about the foods you like to eat. Print a sentence about what kinds of food keep you healthy.

Rule: The letter combination ph has the sound of f. Example: photo sounds like foto. The letter combination alk has the sound of au or aw like you hear in talk or walk.

1 Read the purple word under each picture. Then print it on the line.

cell phone

photo

gopher

elephant

trophy

earphone

2 Draw a line from the word to the picture it matches. Spell the word under each picture.

LESSON 156
Non-Phonetic: ph, alk

Rule: Contractions are single words made by adding two words together, and taking out one or more letters. An apostrophe (') is always used in place of the letter or letters that have been left out.

3 Read the two words that make the contraction. Read the contraction. Underline the letter that has to be left out to make the contraction.

do not → don't
is not → isn't
was not → wasn't

have not → haven't
does not → doesn't
were not → weren't

4 Draw a line between the words that make the contraction.

do not	isn't	have not	doesn't
is not	can't	does not	weren't
can not	don't	were not	haven't

5 Read the two words that make the contraction. Read the contraction. Underline the letters that have to be left out to make the contraction.

I have → I've
she will → she'll
they will → they'll

we have → we've
he will → he'll
it is → it's

6 Talk to your teacher about using a contraction. Think of a sentence about something you can do. Then change it to a sentence about something you can't do. Print it on a piece of paper.

7 Read the sentences. Print a contraction on the blank in place of the two other words.

1. I **have not** seen the moon tonight. ____________

2. John **does not** like to play football. ____________

3. Dad **is not** going to jaywalk on the street. ____________

4. The baby **can not** talk yet. ____________

5. I **do not** have any chalk in my box. ____________

8 Read the sentences with your teacher. Choose the word from the word bank that describes the sentence.

catwalk	sidewalk	jaywalk

1. This is a narrow board on which people walk. ____________

2. It is illegal to walk across the street this way. ____________

3. This is the right place to walk when you are in town. ____________

9 Read the sentences with your teacher. Choose the sentence that describes the word from the word bank. Print the word on the line.

elephant	phone	nephew	dolphin
orphan	typhoon	photo	

1. We saw pictures of the bad storm. ____________
2. This huge animal lives in the zoo. ____________
3. I am glad we have one so I can talk to my friends. ____________
4. The boys look like twins in the picture. ____________
5. A part of the family can be this relative. ____________
6. This person doesn't have a family. ____________
7. These large animals swim in the sea. ____________

Rule: Parts of some words do not follow the phonetic rules, but they do have their own sound. Example: Words with alk in them have the sound we hear in the word walk.

⑩ Read the word under each picture and print it on the line.

talk

walk

chalk

⑪ Draw a line from the picture to the word it matches.

stalk

catwalk

jaywalk

sidewalk

LESSON 157
Non-Phonetic: old, ost, olt

Rule: Parts of some words do not follow the phonetic rules. They have their own sound. Even though there is only one vowel in the word, it makes the long vowel sound.

1 Read the word under each picture and print it on the line.

colt

bolt

post

fold

sold

hostess

2 Draw a line from the word to the picture it matches. Spell the word under the picture.

LESSON 157
Non-Phonetic: old, ost, olt

3 Read the sentences with your teacher. Choose the word from the word bank that describes the sentence. Print the word on the line.

unsold	gold	molt	ghost	colt	post

1. The food was left because the man didn't sell it. ____________

2. The story is about something that isn't real. ____________

3. Men got rich when they dug in the ground for it. ____________

4. It's fun to have a baby horse on the farm. ____________

5. They needed a high one to hang the telephone wires. ____________

6. Chickens lose their feathers each year. ____________

Rule: A verb is a word that shows action or a state of being.

4 Read the action verb below each picture. Print them on the lines below the pictures.

run

jump

push

ride

play

lost

sleep

stop

throw

5 Choose an action verb from the word bank to complete each sentence. Print the word on the blank in the sentence.

fight	run	ride	sleep	play	lost

1. Bill will ________ in the boxing ring.

2. Both of the boys will ________ ball on the team.

3. I can ________ the foot race and win.

4. The baby ________ his shoe.

5. The pony lets us ________ horseback every day.

6. At night we all go to ________ in our own beds.

6 Talk to your teacher about the action verbs: run, jump, trot, sleep, stop. Print a sentence using one of the action verbs.

7 Draw a line from the sentence that matches the picture. Underline the action verb in each sentence.

1. The school kids flew their kites at noon.

2. The baby sleeps in her crib.

3. Hank struck the wall with his car.

4. The vase broke into five parts.

5. Jack ate all the apple pie.

6. We march in most parades.

Rule: Parts of some words do not follow the phonetic rules. They have their own sound. Even though there is only one vowel in the word, it makes the long vowel sound.

1 Read the word under each picture and print it on the line.

wild

mild

wind

child

kind

mind

blind

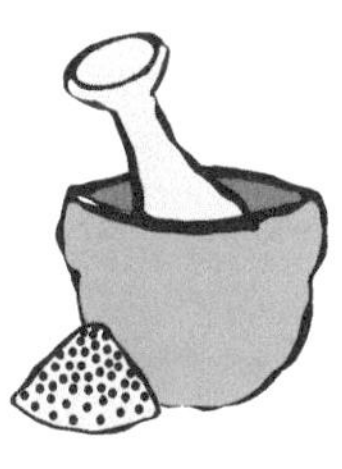
grind

2 Draw a line from the word to the picture it matches. Spell the word under the picture.

child

rind

grind

wild

kind

find

MALL ENTRANCE

LESSON 158
Non-Phonetic: ild, ind

3 **Read the sentences with your teacher. Choose and print the correct word to complete the sentence.**

1. The animals in the zoo are ________. — wind / wild

2. Today when the sun was shining it felt so ________ and nice. — mild / milk

3. We knew the lady was ________ when we saw her white cane. — blind / bind

4. The dentist had to ________ this tooth first. — kind / grind

5. The ________ played on the swings in the park. — child / chime

4 **Underline the pronouns in each sentence.**

She will go to school with her brother.

He can play in the yard with the dog.

They want to go to a show.

We will take the bus to town.

5 Put a circle around the nouns in the sentences. On the line at the end of the sentence print a 1 if the noun is the name of a person; a 2 if the noun is the name of a thing; or a 3 if the noun is the name of a place.

The dog sleeps all day.

Jack likes to read.

Park Street has been snowy this winter.

Fran and Phil are nice.

6 Put a square around the action verbs in the sentences.

Joe caught the baseball.

Jan and Fred walked to school.

The dog jumps high to get the ball.

How many fish swim in your tank?

We always stop at a stop sign.

7 Talk to your teacher about writing your own sentence. Think of a noun and what was happening. Think: who (noun or pronoun) did what (action verb). Be sure to put a capital letter for your beginning word and finish it with the correct punctuation mark. Use another piece of paper to write your sentence.

LESSON 159

Review: Non-Phonetics

1 Look at the pictures. Choose a word from the word bank and print it under the picture it matches.

phone	elephant	colt	gold
child	blind	gopher	hostess

2 Draw a line from the word to the picture it matches. Then spell the word below each picture.

trophy

earphones

mind

grind

elephant

photo

orphan

LESSON 159
Review: Non-Phonetics

3 Circle the missing letters in each word. Write the missing letters on the lines below.

ild old

w

old olt

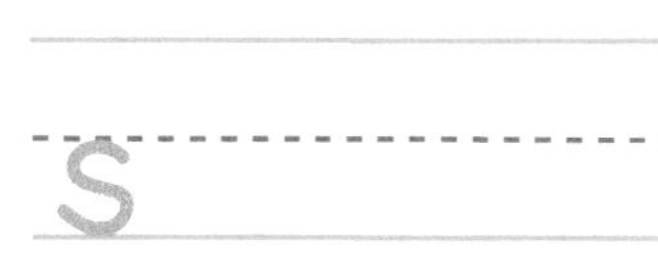

ond ind

olt old

ild olt

c

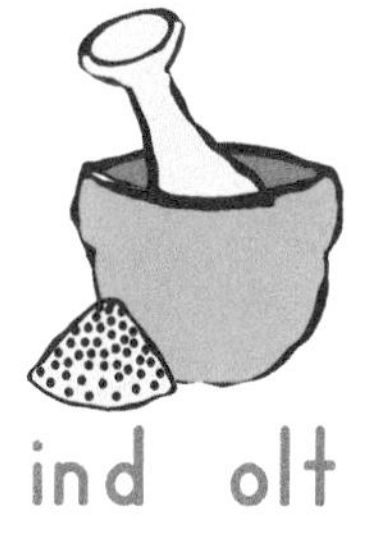

ind olt

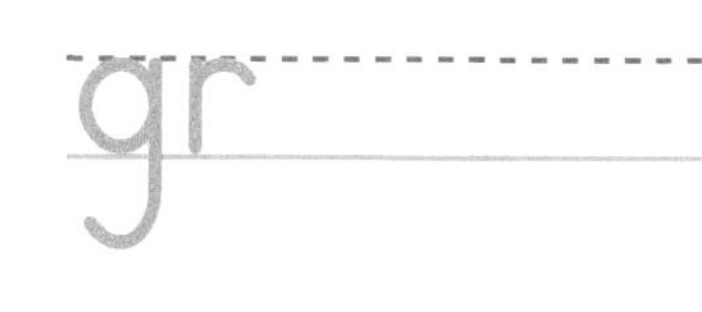

old olt

f

olt ind

bl

4 Use the words in the word bank to complete each sentence.

child	find	colt	hold	kind	grind

1. Jan was ____________ to the lady who was blind.

2. The little ____________ was asleep in her crib.

3. A baby horse is a ____________ .

4. I hope I ____________ my lost shoe.

5. Dad had to ____________ the feed for the cattle.

6. Mom will ____________ the baby in her arms for the photo.

5 Circle the words in the puzzle that are in the word bank.

Across		
child	find	hold

Down		
colt	kind	grind

A	B	C	F	G	E	M	Q	D	C
E	U	B	G	U	Y	R	W	K	V
I	E	N	T	B	U	G	B	I	X
O	M	H	R	W	P	R	L	N	A
U	P	Y	F	R	F	I	N	D	S
X	O	U	V	Z	T	N	P	J	D
Y	L	C	H	I	L	D	H	K	F
Z	K	O	F	X	Z	P	E	L	G
H	O	L	D	S	A	I	O	S	H
D	I	T	E	W	Q	Y	Y	Z	J

6 Read the review words for your teacher.

1.	football	dollar	kitten
2.	spider	basket	fixing
3.	slice	race	giant
4.	elephant	child	blind
5.	mailbox	upstairs	catfish
6.	banking	nice	pencil
7.	large	tiger	phone
8.	mind	colt	cold
9.	most	told	wild

LESSON 160
Review: All

1. Choose the correct letters and spell the words under the pictures.

or ir ar | or ir ar | or ir ar

sk t

or ir ar | or ir ar | or ir ar

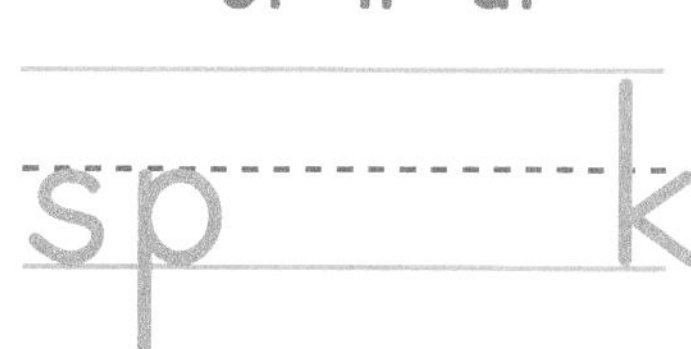

sh t
f k

2. Put a circle around the words that have the long ā sound. Put a square around the words that have the long ē sound.

hay	monkey	day	key	x-ray
play	stay	tray	donkey	pray

3 Choose the correct letters and spell the words under the pictures.

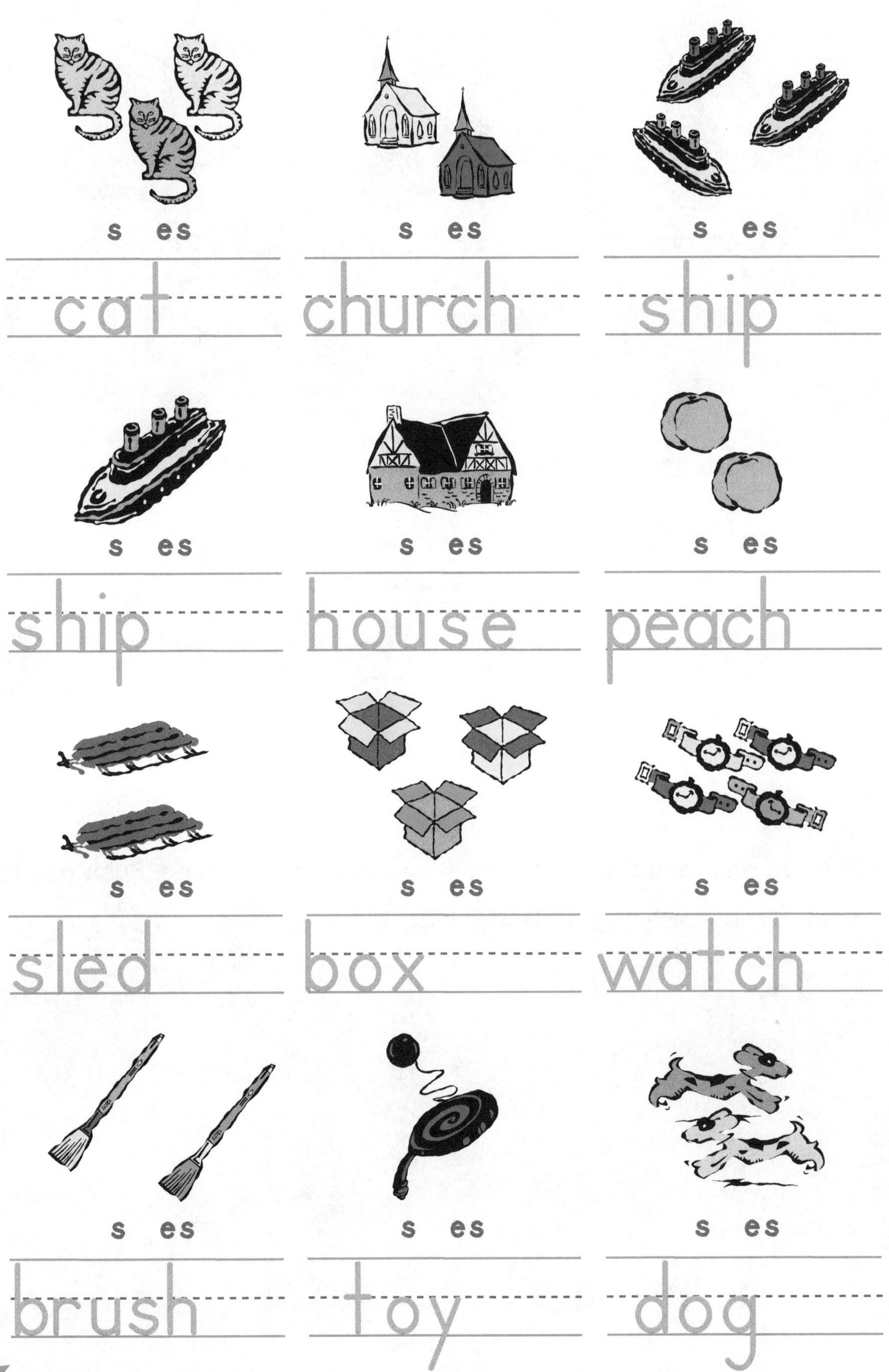

4 Choose the correct letters and spell the words under the pictures. Use y or change the y to i and add es.

baby ies

lady ies

kitty ies

puppy ies

cherry ies

daisy ies

5 Read the words. Put a line between the double consonants in the middle.

button funny rabbit letter rubber

6 Read the words. Put a line between the two syllables divided by two different consonants.

basket harbor number sixteen window

7 Choose the correct letters and spell the words under the pictures.

8 Put a circle around the pictures that have the letter y that makes the long ī sound.

9 Put a square around the pictures that have the letter y that makes the long ē sound.

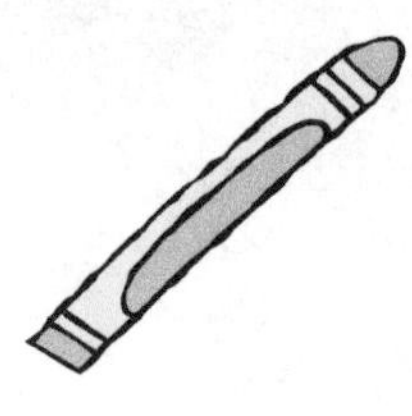

⑩ Draw a line from the picture to the word it matches.

stool

crow

town

clown

mouth

⑪ Draw a line from the picture to the word it matches.

brown

elbow

brook

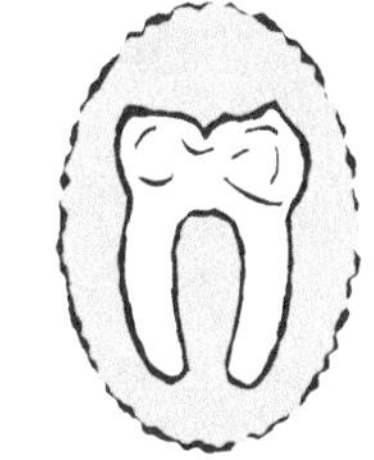

cloud

tooth

⑫ **Draw a line from the picture to the word it matches.**

prawn

shawl

claw

Paul

auto

vault

⑬ **Draw a line from the picture to the word it matches.**

threw

coin

flew

cowboy

toy

joint

LESSON 160
Review: All

14 Read the words. Cross out the silent letter in each word. Draw a line to the picture it matches.

wrist

write

knee

knife

comb

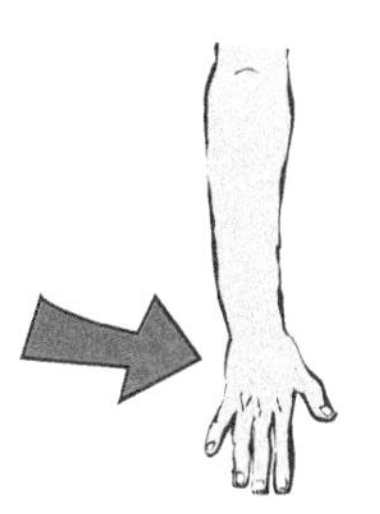

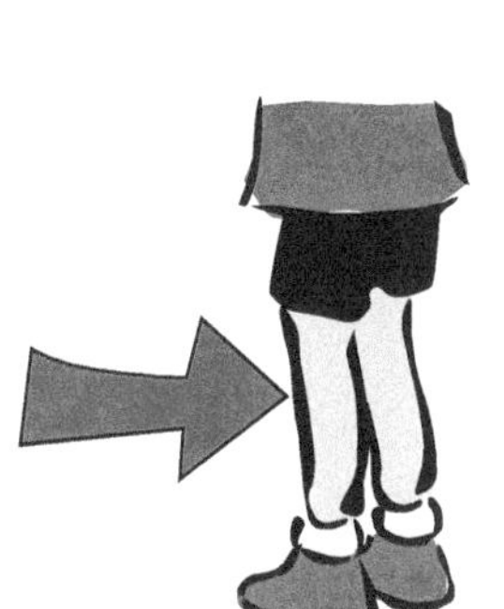

15 Read the words. Cross out the silent letter in each word. Draw a line to the picture it matches.

crumb

gnat

sign

right

night

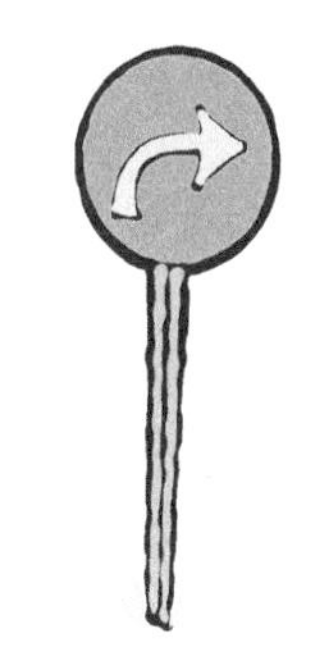

16 Draw a line between the words that make a compound word. Print the words on the lines below.

mail	shoe	flag	brush
book	box	tooth	shine
horse	case	sun	pole

17 Put a circle around the words that have the sound of soft c or g.

cent	crate	price	prince	flat
goat	celery	range	giant	badge

LESSON 160
Review: All

18 Look at the pictures. Choose a word from the word bank and print it under the picture it matches.

trophy	blind	sold	phone	
photo	child	tight	jaywalk	colt

19 Draw a picture of yourself.